I Could Be Wrong

50+ blog posts, short reads, big laughs, wit & wisdom

By Billie Best

Illustrations by Brenda Rose

This book is an anthology of blog posts both fiction and nonfiction authored by Billie Best. The blog may be found at billiebest.com.

First edition November 2020

Paperback ISBN: 978-1-7345964-2-7
Ebook ISBN: 978-1-7345964-3-4

Cover design by Brenda Rose
Illustrations by Brenda Rose

Widowspeak Publishing
3003 W. 11th Avenue, PMB 193
Eugene, OR 97402
www.widowspeakpublishing.com
books@widowspeakpublishing.com

Table of Contents

In Case You Were Wondering 1

1. A Surreal Bending of Time 3

2. The Thickening 7

3. Scientific Method 11

4. Humble Pie 15

5. How to Deal with a Midlife Crisis (Tattoo Planning) .. 19

6. Party Talk 23

7. Cheeseburger Dreams 27

8. Junie 31

9. Immortalia 35

10. Marriage Breakdown After 30 Years 39

11. Church Basements 43

12. The Joy of Doing Nothing 47

13. I Once Had a Sugar Daddy 51

14. Time is Not Money 55

15. Professional Jealousy (Carnita #1) 59

16. The Zen of Betsy Wetsy 63

17. Marlene 67

18. How to Process Grief 71
19. Cupidity 75
20. Vocabulary Lesson 79
21. Hand Cream 83
22. Plan Death Like a Wedding.. 87
23. Girl with the Far Away Eyes 91
24. In the Time of Chairs.. 95
25. Free the Nipple 99
26. Solo Flight (Senior and Single).. 103
27. My Ugly Shoes.. 107
28. How to Move Forward After Becoming a Widow.. 111
29. True Confessions.. 115
30. Click This.. 119
31. Queen of the House.. 123
32. Thinking Off the Grid.. 127
33. Good Girl, Bad Girl 131
34. The Cooking Lesson (Carnita #2).. 135
35. The Lady Belcher 139
36. How to Downsize & Start Over.. 143
37. Swipe Left 147

38. Hot Flash Fiction 151
39. Inhale Exhale 155
40. Pancakes – a modern parable 159
41. Date with a Spider 163
42. Black Hole 167
43. Fear of Forgetting 171
44. Our Collective Diapers 175
45. I Shaved My Legs 179
46. My Menopause Conspiracy Theory 183
47. I Could Be Wrong 187
48. Speed Dating 191
49. Call Me Penguin 195
50. The Cure for Ageism 199
51. Perfecting My Ignorance 203
52. The Nipple Club (Carnita #3) 207
53. High Risk Behavior 211
54. Anniversary of Hope 215

In Case You Were Wondering

The 54 blog posts in this anthology were written between January 2019 and October 2020, published each Wednesday on my website, billiebest.com, emailed to subscribers, and posted on Facebook. I started the blog without direction or narrowing my subject because I wanted to develop my skills as a writer and explore my possibilities for an audience. What I found was you. Thousands of you. And that makes me really, really happy. So, thank you. Thank you for reading my words and encouraging me to write.

Each post reflects my thinking on our life and times, the experience of aging (I'm 66), menopause and the power of women in midlife, and the changes that build our strength and resilience as we evolve through them. Some of the posts are quite sober, but most are just for fun, adult humor, wit and wisdom. For your amusement, each post includes an imaginary tarot card illustrated by my talented friend, Brenda Rose, because, as you know, aging well is all about how you play your cards.

Consider keeping this book in your bathroom beside the throne as one of many avenues toward self-help. And don't take me too seriously. I could be wrong.

— Billie Best

VI
TIME TRAVELER

1. A Surreal Bending of Time

I'm stuck in a surreal bending of time. My calendar is empty for the rest of my life, or at least until this situation sorts itself out, which I now realize could be many months. I shudder and focus on the things I can control, like setting the microwave for 90 seconds and refilling ice cube trays. My day is occupied by the excruciating mundane, washing my hands, washing my masks, washing dishes, feeding the dog, walking the dog. I never washed so many dishes because I never ate so many meals at home. I bought some new plastic containers to hold my leftovers in the fridge. Someday I hope to give them away as a sign that my life is back to normal and I don't have to eat chili five meals in a row. But for now, that's just how it is, and I feel self-conscious for complaining because I'm fortunate enough to make too much chili and eat it for a week. Still, eating the same thing every day erases my memory of what day it is. Today could definitely be yesterday or tomorrow. How would I know?

My isolation is a weird mix of being disconnected from the things I enjoy and feeling deeply connected to the fierce humans who share my fate. A new world is being formed by the invisible hand of unity. If this calamity was an earthquake or a hurricane, it would be localized, we could picture the phenomenon and comprehend the destruction. We could calculate the total loss and plan the process of rebuilding. But so much of what is changing these days is metaphysical: our knowledge, our beliefs, our sense of self, our relationships, our habits, our commitments, our sense of place, our values, our priorities. Our routines have been disrupted by uncertainty and our confidence in the system is shaken. Seven billion of us are re-ordering our lives based on new information, moving like a school of anchovies in synchronous fear to evade the shark. Seven billion moments in time become one shared reality. One history. One humanity. One future.

I watch the digital clock on the microwave, and it seems to be moving slower than it did a month ago. Minutes have more space between them. I suspect a surreal bending of time like when your car fishtails on a slick road and you feel your guts swishing from side to side between your ribs, and you know you're out of control, and your whole life passes before you because you're pretty sure you're going to wake up dead, and then your front fender hits a guard rail and your tires grip the land and the fishtail stops, but the adrenaline keeps rushing and you have visions of end times so profound that you'll never be the same again, and you promise yourself you'll be kind to every person you meet for the rest of your life.

I imagine humanity mid fishtail, in a blur of the mundane and the profound, a surreal bending of time punctured by the ding of my microwave. Lunch is ready. I listen to a podcast. I eat. I brush my teeth. The math of toilet paper shortages commingles with the math of illness and death, and I promise myself, if I live through this, I'll be kind to every person I meet for the rest of my life, and next time, I won't make so much chili.

I Could Be Wrong

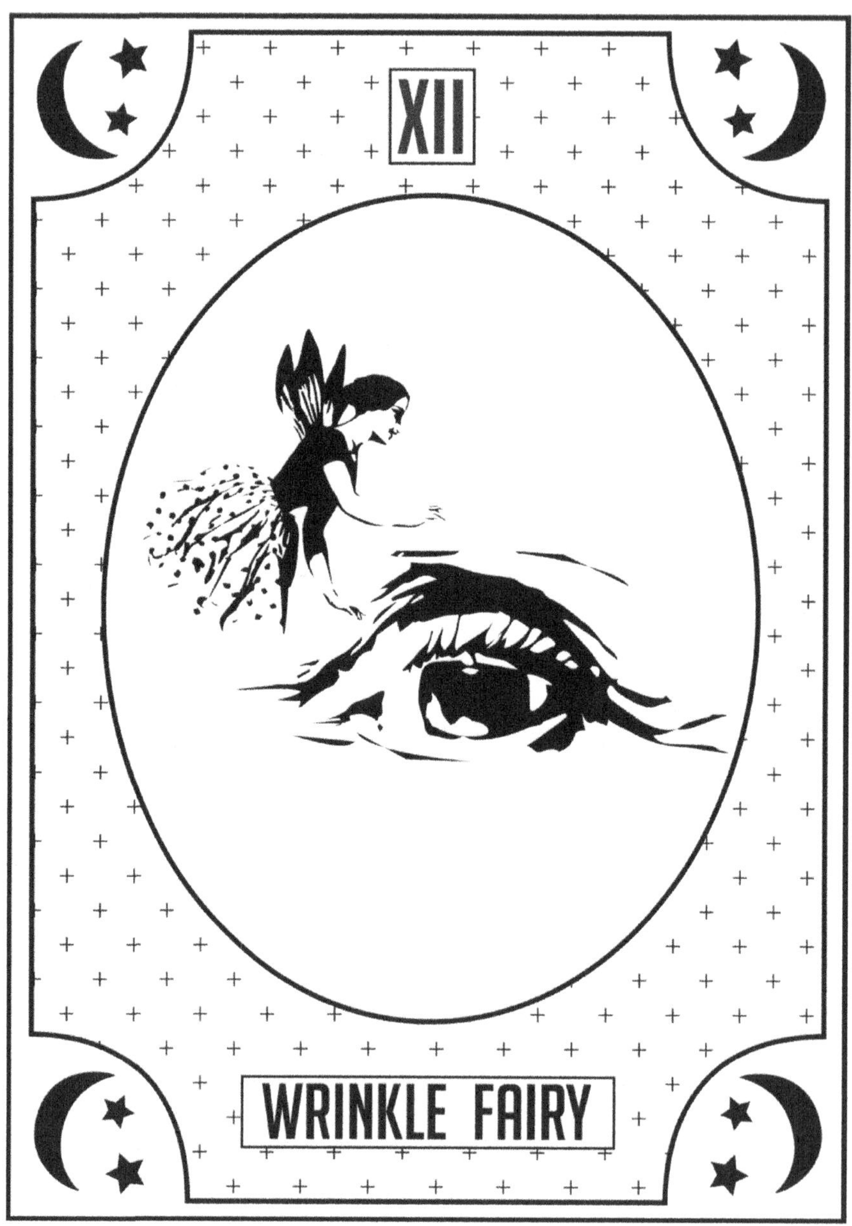
XII
WRINKLE FAIRY

2. The Thickening

Fairies broke into my bedroom while I was sleeping and inflated my waistline. That's the only explanation I can think of for the thickening around my middle. It seemed to happen overnight. One day I woke up and there was all this extra me. In a life where so many things have slowed, my body seems to be changing really fast. I have new spots on my face daily, and the wrinkles around my mouth suck my lipstick up my nose.

As a young girl I stood in front of the mirror wishing my boobs would grow, puffing up my chest, hoping for more. Fifty years later I'd like to give some of that back. A lifetime of fashion magazines has taught me that big boobs are fine for sex workers and Hollywood movies. But clothes hang more elegantly on women passed over by the Boob Fairy.

About the same time as the thickening of my waist, my breasts ballooned into button popping mounds that want to spill over the top of my bra and bounce on my ribs. If they were torpedoes, I'd be in danger of shooting myself in the foot. My clothes don't fit the way they used to. I starve myself to try to reverse the process, but this new shape seems to be permanent — and I really like food. I think I remember my mother looking this way, but I never thought it would happen to me.

Our whole lives our bodies do things we wish they wouldn't. Nature has the final word, but she doesn't choose what's fashionable. I'd like to pretend I spent a fortune having these lines carved into my forehead. I went to a day spa to have these spots tinted on my hands. My moles were sculpted. My hairdresser took hours dyeing one hair at a time to make these grey highlights. But the truth is I did not curate my look. I woke up like this.

How different my experience of aging would be if I could see myself on the cover of a magazine in the checkout line at the grocery store. Headline: 10 Ways to Make Your Wrinkles Shine. Subhead: Turtlenecks are in!

I imagine overhearing someone in line behind me say, "Wow, her wrinkles are really cool."

I want to see women who look like me in the media montage of celebrities, heroes and entrepreneurs. My aging face is not the failure of cosmetics. It's a statement about self-confidence that says aging is cool. I'm aging by design. This look is earned, not made. You can't buy these wrinkles. You have to wait for the Wrinkle Fairy to visit you in the night.

I Could Be Wrong

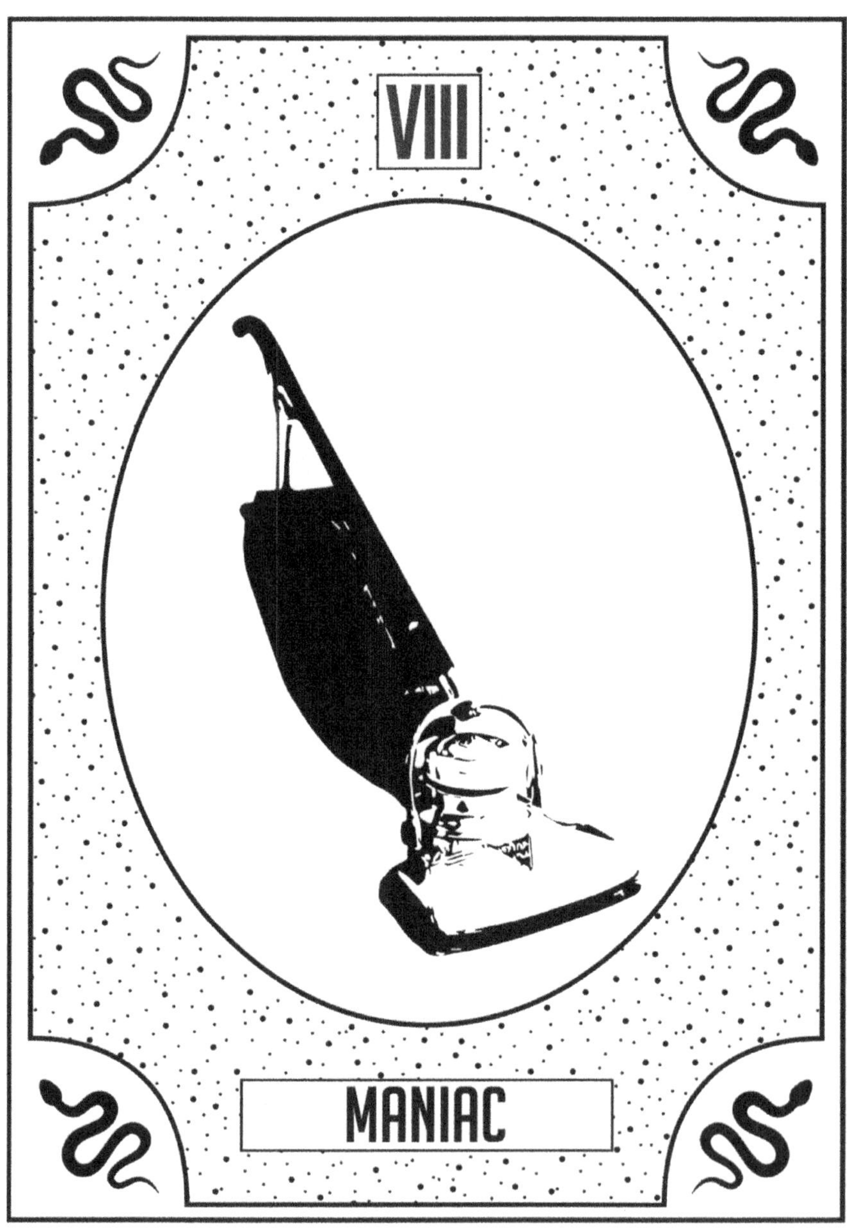
VIII
MANIAC

3. Scientific Method

I'm doing a scientific study in my apartment, tracking the lifecycle of a dust bunny, trying to understand how they reproduce so quickly. As we enter the age of the Sixth Extinction, I think it's important to witness the habitat of other animals and our impact on their survival. I've chosen dust bunnies as a case study because we inhabit the same ecosystem, and I find the process of their population growth perplexing. So, I'm going to try to learn more about them.

The thing that's so counterintuitive about the dust bunny lifecycle is that removing the adults doesn't seem to stop the children from appearing. Baby dust bunnies seem to come from nowhere. How is that possible? For most species, if you kill off all the adults, they can't multiply, and the species will become extinct. But I kill dust bunnies ruthlessly, and when I turn around, there they are again. My life is like an episode of the Twilight Zone. I'm being stalked by zombie hairballs.

Now I'm realizing I may need another more experienced investigator to advise me on my work. So, I've sent an invitation to David Attenborough to come to my apartment for tea. There are so many questions I want to ask him. Do dust bunnies experience anger? Because the way they stick to my socks seems hostile. Can they hear? Because I've noticed when my dog runs through the room, they seem to tumble away from him in all directions. Why are they all the same color? And why do the adults seem to reach a point where they gain weight and lose their shape? Do dust bunnies experience menopause?

A warren of dust bunnies lives under my furniture. I watch them from across the room with a pair of binoculars, making notes in my journal. They seem to prefer sheltered places, under the bed, under my desk, under the shoe rack in my closet. They lounge there still as stones until my dog's ball rolls by. Then suddenly they sink themselves into the outer coating of dog saliva, until in a matter of seconds they've stopped the ball and covered the bright orange like dry land leeches. It's disgusting, but I'm getting used to the brutality of Nature. Every smear of dog saliva in my apartment seems to attract hungry dust bunnies. Law of the jungle, I guess.

I've pinned a couple adult specimens on a sample board so I can examine their anatomy more closely and I bought a complicated software program to track the microchips I intend to implant in a few of the adults. Now I'm reading the user manual while I wait for David Attenborough to return my call. He's going to be very impressed with my scientific method. It's kind of exciting. I feel like I'm at the beginning of something big. It could take years. But I'll do anything to avoid vacuuming my apartment.

I Could Be Wrong

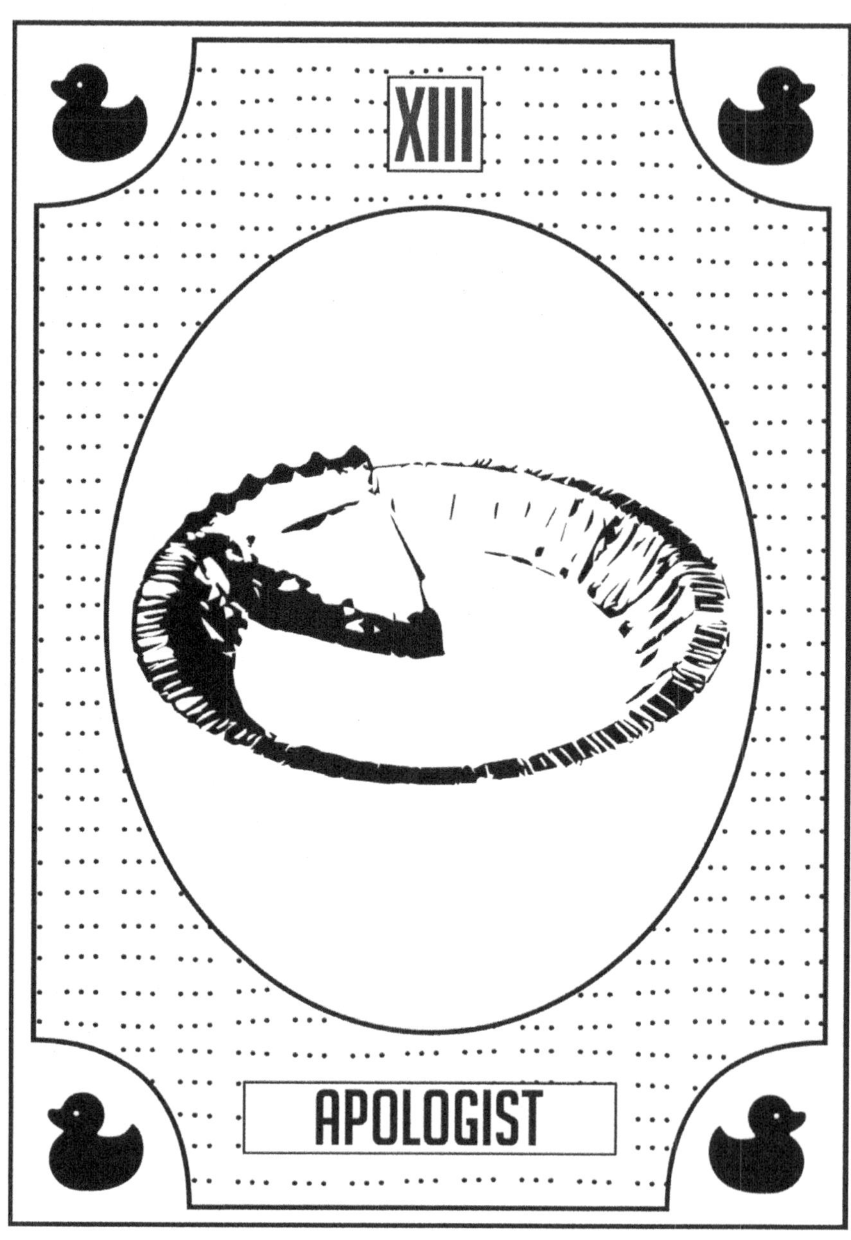
XIII
APOLOGIST

4. Humble Pie

I always sound like I know what I'm talking about. That's my biggest flaw. I lack humility. My point of view is absolute. I don't allow for the possibility of being incorrect. This kind of arrogance plays out beautifully in my imagination. I make a profound statement. My audience gasps in awe at my genius. A lone detractor raises his voice to challenge me — yes, it's always a guy I'm arguing with, probably my father. I muster the perfectly phrased retort, my challenger drops to his knees in abject submission, and I do a victory lap around my desk. In my mind I always win.

It's more of a challenge to be right all the time in real life. On social media I type a flip remark into a comment box with great self-satisfaction, not realizing how cringe worthy it reads until days later when I'm very thankful for the Delete function. But there is no Delete function to protect me from myself at a dinner party or when I'm walking my dog. Times like that are risky for me because I often hold points of view like racehorses waiting at the gate to gallop forth from my mouth.

So, as I'm walking my dog, Moon, on Sunday morning, a handsome young man in a navy-blue double-breasted coat and Gucci slippers is bending over to scoop up his dog's pile when his tiny fur ball charges Moon, who weighs 80 lbs.

"My dog could kill your dog," I snapped. "Your dog should be on a leash. A dog isn't a worm, you know. It needs discipline."

Points of view revealed: little dogs bark too much, people treat little dogs like infants, people don't train their dogs properly. It was a lot to unpack before his first Mimosa. His face turned red, his eyes watered, and he sniffed. I thought he might cry as he picked up his itty-bitty canine, mumbled an apology, and walked away.

I'm at least 30 years older than he is, maybe 40, but I don't see myself that way. I don't see myself as an old crank. On the inside I'm the same smart aleck I've been since high school. I don't think about how my age gives character to my words. He could have told me to go F myself, but he was embarrassed and respectful. It was his humility that made me feel awful. But it was too late to take it back. So, I'm saying my apology here now as I choke down this humble pie.

I Could Be Wrong

X
BOMBER

5. How to Deal with a Midlife Crisis (Tattoo Planning)

I did not know how to deal with a midlife crisis. In my mind it wasn't happening. I was just changing the way I had been living for the past 20 years. The things I thought would make me happy — money, career success, status — had lost their sizzle. My job, the way I earned money, felt obligatory. I was just going through the motions. Work didn't satisfy me anymore. My midlife crisis wasn't postpartum blues for the loss of my youth. At 50, I was feeling my Titanic expectations for adulthood crash against the mundane iceberg of my reality. Note to self, a common misperception of adulthood is that you know what you're doing. Then you find out you don't.

My need for change was basic. All I wanted to do was blow up my life and start over with pursuits that felt more meaningful than writing formulas in an Excel spreadsheet. I wanted to live off the grid. Not without electricity, without math. I started a farm, traded PowerPoint for a wheelbarrow and a manure shovel, learned to grow potatoes, shook off the *Wall Street Journal* and started reading the *Farmer's Almanac*. Then I put a mini fridge on the front porch to sell eggs in an honor system farm store with a glass jar for the money. The honor system was my new religion.

Unfortunately, I could not pay my mortgage in free range chicken and grassfed beef. To sustain my irrational exuberance for farming I drained my retirement accounts, cashed in my life insurance policy and maxed out my credit cards. Eventually, the only way out of all that debt was to sell the farm. Farming was the most rewarding work I have ever done, but financially I would have been better off chained to a computer in a cubicle at the office.

Learning how to deal with a midlife crisis was challenging, not unlike the other seminal events of midlife, menopause and sexual dysfunction. We were made to go through these changes, but we don't get much encouragement to learn about them. There's no adult education class on How to Have a Super Midlife Crisis. Of course, midlife is different for everyone, and much of what we experience is cultural. Some say the modern midlife crisis isn't real, or it's only for the middle class, or it's only for men. But it seems natural to me that midway through our lives we would want to assess our progress and re-evaluate our plans. It makes sense that maturity would impact our goals and objectives. Correcting the course of our lives by making different choices seems practical. Perhaps our biggest challenge in midlife is resistance to change.

I'm a person with the opposite problem. I thrive on change. It exhilarates me. I don't regret crushing my professional lifestyle in the name of agricultural idealism. It was a great adventure. I'm stronger now, more resilient, and better equipped for an uncertain future. In fact, now that I know how to deal with a midlife crisis, I'm expecting a late life crisis. Probably around the time I'm 80 I'll have the feeling that I've made all the wrong choices again, napping when I should be learning to play the tuba. That's when I'm going to buy a little red sports car, start dating younger men, and get a tattoo on my left breast that says, Oops!

I Could Be Wrong

II
DRINKER

6. Party Talk

I went to a farm party where the high point of the evening was chicken shit bingo. A single chicken was placed in a large cage over a giant bingo board, and the numbers on the board were purchased by the party goers to benefit the arts. When the hen shat on a lucky number, the crowd roared, and the winner walked off with a lovely gift basket. A lot of wine was involved, and it was good fun for everyone but the hen.

On the other side of the barnyard, I stood at the wine bar and noticed the woman beside me had glassy tears in her eyes. "I hate it when people are mean to chickens," she said, her crystal earrings twinkling in the light. I smiled and nodded. I had had my own flock of chickens for 13 years, and although the bingo concept was pretty cool, my sympathies were with the hen.

"We had chickens when I was growing up," she said. "And our rooster was blind. So, my dad refused to feed it. That made me really sad." She squeezed out a tear. "So, I fed the rooster when my dad wasn't looking, and after a while he started following me around."

"Your dad?" I asked.

She blinked and teetered. I could see she realized something was wrong with her story, but she couldn't quite grasp it. "No," she said. "The rooster. He followed me everywhere."

We were clustered beside a row of tomato plants, under carnival lights strung from a work shed to a garden post. It was a starry summer evening. A blue grass band played in the gazebo, and a hundred revelers roamed about, sipping festive beverages, feeling farmish. The bingo players were hollering at the chicken, waving their arms in the air, cheering for their numbers. But she was in a different world now.

"We would meet behind the garage and I would feed him." Her eyes swept the night sky, searching fruitlessly until she sighed, suddenly overcome. "I loved that rooster," she gasped. "Of course, my dad never knew. He would have been so angry with me. But I couldn't stop feeding him just because he was blind."

She looked me in the eye to be sure I appreciated her dilemma. Then she tilted her head back and drained her glass. Wet mascara rolled down her cheeks to her chin. "Well, maybe he wasn't that blind," she said, catching up with herself. "He was just partly blind. But he couldn't see that well. I had to feed him. He needed me." She began to move in the direction of the bar. Then she turned back to me and grabbed my arm.

"Love is crazy, isn't it? I mean, when you really stop and think about it. It's just crazy."

I felt the burn of wine in my nostrils and swallowed hard. "Yes, it is." I raised my glass to her. "Just crazy."

I Could Be Wrong

WILD CARD
PEE BREAK

7. Cheeseburger Dreams

I went through menopause years ago, but if I want to trigger a flashback all I have to do is eat a bacon cheeseburger and chase it with a few shots of bourbon. That metabolism disrupting indulgence can have me wide awake in the middle of the night between damp sheets, remembering the good old days of cannonball mood swings, losing my car keys, and wasabi hot flashes. Now menstruation is getting some good PR with women producing a documentary film called *Period. End of Sentence.* about the social taboo of becoming a woman, and I'm thinking we need a film called *End of Period. New Sentence.* about the joy of life after menstruation.

Menopause could use some good PR. Modern medicine has characterized the end of menstruation as an illness, but with the help of functional fabric and techno-fashion designers we could spin it as a time of self-expression, wearing our hormone changes like peacocks instead of fussing over sweat stains. Picture yourself in a mood dress of thermo-chromic silk that changes color with your state of mind, or a heat detecting jacket that lights up and blinks before a hotflash, or robotic socks that remember where you were ten minutes ago.

These days girls are having parties to celebrate their first period with red decorations, feminine paraphernalia, and red cake. I'm imagining a menopause party where we all wear our mood dresses. First prize goes to the woman who can stay beige the longest. Then we'll turn off the lights and watch our hotflash jackets blink in the dark. Why hasn't technology caught up with menopause? There should be an iMenopause ecosystem of apps and apparel, GIFs and emojis, virtual assistants and wrist bots.

Menopause is all about managing our biometrics. I want a pair of wired granny panties that come with earbuds to track my pulse, hormones, fluids and temperature. The earbuds would whisper messages like, "Hot flash in 60 seconds. Prepare to peel." Or "Get out now before you say something you regret." Or "Order the salad. Order the salad." Or in a real emergency, "Leak warning! Your bladder is 90% full. Find a restroom now!"

And about that voice — The smug self-confidence and pseudo cheerfulness of virtual assistants is annoying. I don't want to be bossed around by some young twerp. I'd like a cranky old lady voice that drips with irony and offers unsolicited advice. When I'm driving down the highway asking for directions to the nearest Burgerville, she would say, "So you don't need to sleep tonight? Because the last time you went to Burgerville for dinner you were scrolling through Instagram at two o'clock in the morning." Then at two o'clock in the morning she would say, "I told you to order the salad. Maybe next time you'll listen." And, I'll think yes, yes, of course you're right, because I'm wide awake now and this is my cheeseburger dream.

I Could Be Wrong

V
CRONE

8. Junie

My friend Junie was born in the 1890s. When I sat at her table, my young legs barely touched the floor and the world opened up to me through a secret passageway. Her wrinkles were so deep they could grow corn. Long crisscrossed lines cut her cheeks and sliced into her lips, canoes of droopy skin folded around her eyes, and when she laughed her face crumpled like crushed paper. I don't remember her words. Her wisdom may have been beyond my reach. But I felt something flow from her then that gave me a lifelong connection to her strength. She enjoyed solitude.

To get to her house I walked the shore path around Big Bearskin Lake from my grandparent's cottage to Junie's tiny cabin in the trees. She had a long history in that place, but by the time I knew her, she was living alone, wearing clothes her family left behind, sitting on mismatched furniture in a room hung with faded treasures, walking to get firewood in her dead husband's work boots, wearing three pairs of socks, fingers gnarled like turkey feet, silver hair swirling out of a bandana into curls around her face, in a calico dress covered by a plaid apron, wearing a flannel shirt until noon when the sun finally hit her windows. I never thought of her as being poor, but I see now that she was.

My grandmother often sent me to Junie's with a basket of vegetables from her garden, a jar or two of some jam or chicken-in-aspic she put up herself, and sometimes an envelope of seeds. My grandmother and Junie were seed savers. They knew the lifecycle of the plants in their garden. They watched and waited for the seeds to age and cure. Then they stored them in envelopes wrapped with rubber bands and labeled in pencil with the plant name and the year. This was my introduction to the cycle of life, my keepsake of sacred knowledge from the women who showed me the way.

A little girl woven into the lives of elder women picks up a sense of what life becomes, the benevolence of time, and the mystery of joy. When I went to visit Junie, she was always delighted to see me and together we did the tasks of her day. We collected sticks for kindling, made a fire in the woodstove, boiled water for tea, toasted bread over an open flame, poured the leftover hot water into the dirty dishes in the sink, sat face to face at her table, and watched the sun glitter on the lake. It was time she gave me, her presence, her thoughtful listening and focus. She made me feel like my words mattered. I was just a child, but I see now that she was nurturing the woman inside.

I Could Be Wrong

VII
DINOSAUR

9. Immortalia

Remember the story of Rip Van Winkle, an old guy who has a few drinks, falls asleep in the mountains, and wakes up 20 years later when he doesn't know anyone, no one knows him, all his friends are dead, and the world doesn't make sense because he slept through the war that changed everything. Now imagine paying $200,000 to do that and waking up 100 years later. That's cryonic preservation. Instead of falling asleep you have to die first, preferably near a pile of dry ice, then they fill you with liquid antifreeze, like the kind you put in your car, and you stay suspended in a tube of goo in a freezer for a century.

There's only one itty bitty problem with cryonic preservation. The technology for reviving you hasn't been invented yet. They haven't even done it with a mouse or a dog or a monkey. Seriously, anyone who's ever defrosted their freezer should be skeptical. But the cryonic preservation companies are asking you to trust them. What could possibly go wrong?

Frankly, a slick advertising campaign can sell almost anything. Imagine a stylish elderly couple on the beach holding hands as they stroll toward an orange sunset, smiling. Then we see them side-by-side on tables in a swank health spa, still holding hands and smiling. Then we see their family waving to them as they float inside their suspension tube, frozen in their swimsuits, still holding hands and smiling.

Voice over: "Don't say goodbye to love. With Immortalia the future is always possible. Our patented suspension technology will transport you through the years to new horizons only you can imagine. So, say goodbye to death and hello to a place where the sunsets never end. Immortalia."

Then we see the couple thawed out and drippy, walking on the beach again in the same swimsuits. Disclaimer: "Some preservation injury may occur, including organ failure, mushy facial features, hair loss, blindness, memory loss, dementia, depression, amnesia, neuropathy, brain damage, cardiac arrest, nausea, diarrhea, and paralysis. Death must occur naturally. Microbiome replacement may cause mood swings. If you have suicidal thoughts contact your physician. Some patients may remain in a vegetative state. Terms and conditions apply. Revival not guaranteed."

Are you sold? Me neither. Aside from the obvious unproven business model, the absence of the revival technology, and the fact that a power failure could turn me into pudding, I think the cryonic preservationists have failed to answer one really big question: WHY?

Why would I want to live to be 165 in a world where my iPhone doesn't work, and all my friends are dead? Who will know me and care about me? I may not even recognize myself. What good is that? Please, just give me a natural elderhood where I can live in the slow lane until I stop. I'm very happy to take my chances on life the old-fashioned way.

I Could Be Wrong

II
MEDIATOR

10. Marriage Breakdown After 30 Years

I never expected a marriage breakdown after 30 years of being together. I took my marriage for granted, thought it would be there forever, never doubting the strength and resilience of our union. My brain was so locked into the routine of everyday life that I didn't see my husband's patterns of behavior changing until he had already drifted far from me. Now that situation is in my rearview mirror and I have a fresh perspective on why it happened. With perfect hindsight I can see our marriage breakdown after 30 years was bound to happen because our careers were going in opposite directions. In midlife our goals changed, and we wanted different things.

Anything can become routine if you do it for 30 years, even great sex. We became accustomed to the rhythm of our lives and we didn't notice subtle changes until they added up to something big. My husband and I had an arrangement that I would be the breadwinner and he would be the home caretaker because he was an artist without the chops to bring home a big paycheck, and I had an instinct for business that gave me a competitive edge at the office. We always lived in beautiful places. He had the skills to build it. I paid for it. Then when I was 47, I changed my mind about work.

Like millions of other middle-aged people, after 9/11 I had an epiphany about how I was spending my time. If the world was to end in a heartbeat, would I be pleased to look back at my bank balance, or did I want a more meaningful legacy? That's when I became infected with farming and it took over my life. At the same time my husband had taken his first straight job with a weekly paycheck, full healthcare benefits, a retirement plan and paid vacation. He was like a kid who just discovered sugar at the same time I was going on a diet.

The big change in the way we spent our time every day was a paradigm shift for both of us. Our heads were spinning in opposite directions. The first fights were about money. I had decided I didn't care about it anymore while he was getting high on bringing home the bacon. After a while money was all we ever talked about. The problem as he saw it was that I was spending his paycheck to buy cows. The problem as I saw it was all I wanted to do was become a farmer. I had paid his way as an artist and I wanted him to pay my way as a farmer. Maybe that would have been a fair trade in our 20s, but we were in our 50s. He thought it was too late in our lives to follow farm dreams. And me, well, I'm a dreamer.

Our marriage breakdown after 30 years was ignited by the issue of money. Our ambitions changed and we lost sight of each other. It's an issue we never resolved. Within a few years he was a very sick man, I was his caregiver, and we reunited to prepare for his death. Thankfully for both of us, we didn't split up when things fell apart, we stayed in the marriage, and that gave us the opportunity to evolve back to being in love again just in time to say goodbye.

I Could Be Wrong

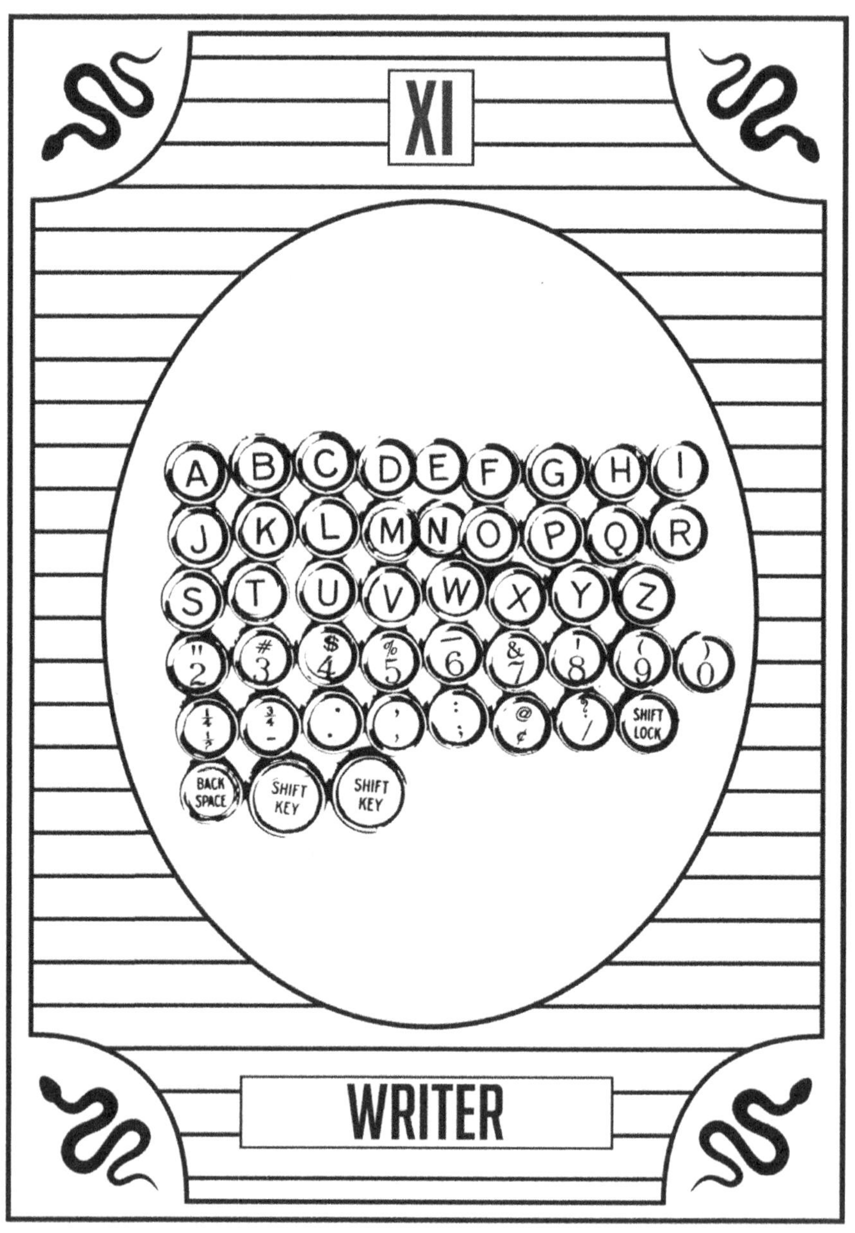
XI
A B C D E F G H I
J K L M N O P Q R
S T U V W X Y Z
" 2 # 3 $ 4 % 5 — 6 & 7 ! 8 (9) 0
SHIFT LOCK
BACK SPACE
SHIFT KEY
SHIFT KEY
WRITER

11. Church Basements

I think people are more civilized in church basements. Maybe it's the aroma of bad coffee and instant cookies, breath mints and air freshener, worn carpeting under fluorescent lights, dusty curtains fanned by swinging doors. So many nonreligious groups meet in church basements. AA meetings, Weight Watchers, anonymous this, anonymous that, group therapy, survivors, knitters, readers, writers, philosophizers and collectors, sitting in folding chairs, speaking in reasonable tones. Church basements are a place for those interstitial emotions, nothing too extreme, affinities in the public domain, skills learned at summer camp, lifetime interests, thoughtful consideration of a hobby or a habit.

It's a naturally slow space. There's really nowhere to race off to in a church basement. No speed dating, no eating contests, no stock trades, no yelling, no privacy. Life meanders politely, eyes meet, pleasantries are exchanged, civilization is tamped down to a well-worn path. Odors rise unremarked. No fart jokes in a church basement, nothing obtrusive. Just adults mixed with sugar.

I'm sitting at a meeting of writers because I think I'll learn something. The room vibrates with low voices, chairs scraping, people settling in like a flock of geese on old corn. Two women behind me swap stories about their Disney vacations. A scattered group of men kibitz about whether it's possible to write a book about crime without any professional experience in law-and-order. The ex-CIA guy doesn't think so. The hippy guy thinks absolutely so. They debate whether getting arrested is a law-and-order experience. I shouldn't turn around and look, but I sneak a look anyway.

Some guy chimes in on the law-and-order discussion with the idea of writing what you know. Evidently, he's struggling to write good porn because he's been happily married for 30 years. My ears practically bend off my head. I want to change my seat and move closer to them so I can hear better. Are they really talking about porn? Another guy pipes up and says, yes, write what you know, but lie about it if necessary. Then another guy says be creative, use your imagination, and lie, lie, lie. I decide not to change seats in case they get struck by lightning. We are after all in a church basement. I'm sure somebody upstairs is listening.

There are refreshments in the kitchen across the room, but I'm skipping the snacks because I don't want to miss anything. The two women compare how lovely Disney World is at twilight, the castles, when the breeze lifts the heat and the sky glows. Nice. Very literary. I smell stale cigarettes and imagine smoke clinging to an old sweater somewhere. Then a youngish guy behind me is sad. He says he's never written anything less than 100,000 words. A proofreader gasps. He can't stop himself from writing. He calls it verbal diarrhea, a mental infection. That's when I realize, oh, this meeting is about addiction. I'm with a group of people addicted to the alphabet.

I Could Be Wrong

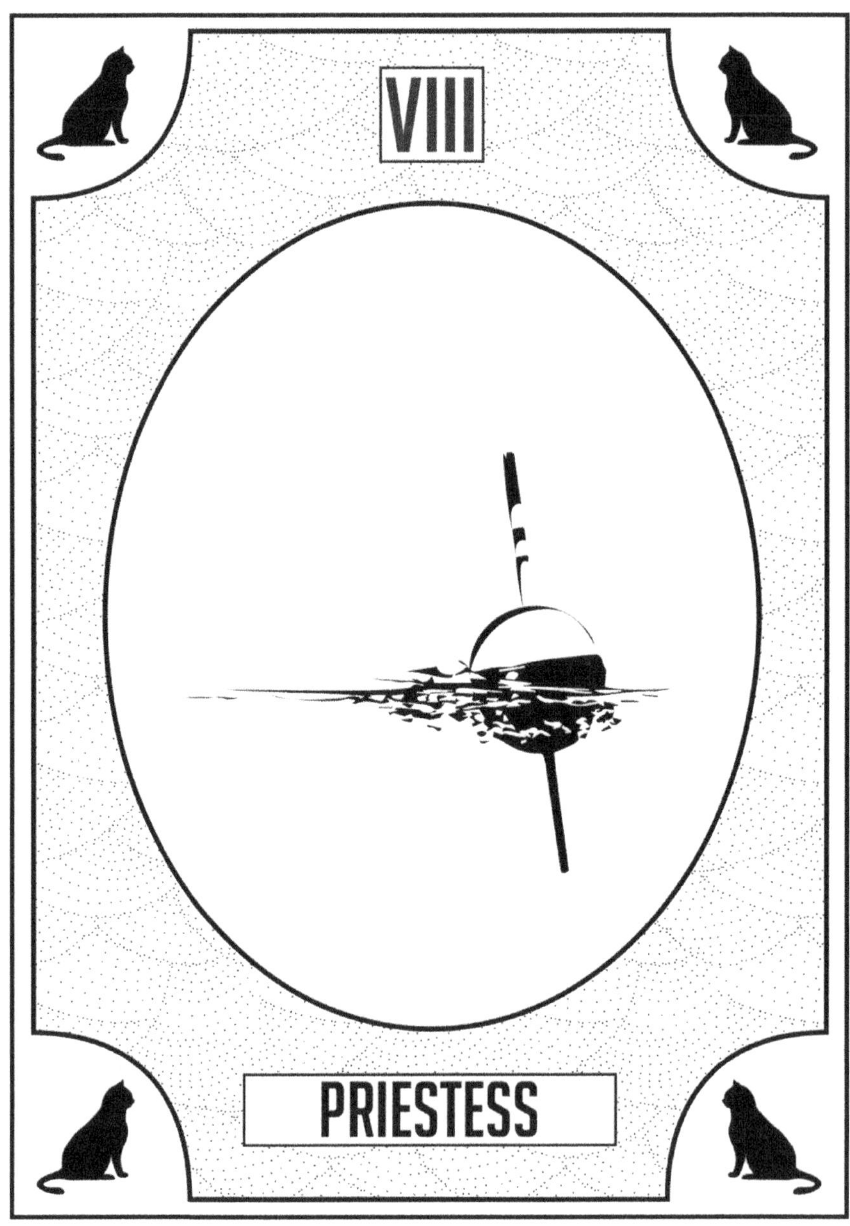
VIII
PRIESTESS

12. The Joy of Doing Nothing

Sunday morning on the river there were dozens of small boats floating in silent meditation like lotus flowers with their buddha fishermen seated plump and low, poles dangling lines in the water, catch and release, a rite of spring. It was as though I had stepped through a shimmering doorway into heaven. Serene as monks they murmured affectionately to their comrades and waved open hands across the water to their neighbors. The birds were delirious with song and among them I heard a voice say, *There was never a more perfect day, We have everything we need, Tomorrow will take care of itself.*

The air carried the scent of earth and rain, flowering trees dropped their petals on the breeze, pigeons cooed in their nooks on the seawall, and I felt an unqualified good inside. Like *Wow*! good. Maybe it was the caffeine, but my inner prism caught the sun, a rainbow arched through my chest, and my heart tap danced. *I'm doing okay*, I thought. *How is that even possible? Where am I?*

The power of feeling good overwhelmed me and I saw how I had been settled into a mental rut expecting to be dissatisfied far into the future, and here I was completely filled with wonder and hippie-dippy love for mankind. The fishermen seemed immortal Masters of the Universe, drifting calmly through unspeakable tensions and disappointments, gliding along a ribbon of wild water under a splendid sky, superheroes on vacation, stretching their legs and snoozing behind sunglasses. This kind of fishing really isn't about the fish. Still as tombstones, leaning back against the cooler in duckbill hats, hands folded across the belly, oil stained boots resting on seat cushions, munching donuts with cold coffee — it's not what you expect from an apex predator.

On the wharf I sat down and immersed myself in the timeless elegance of waiting for fish, the wealth of rivers and the spiritual healing of sunshine. This slow motion dragging of a hook in the water seemed to be less a sport than a religious ritual, a communion of souls with the life force, a reassurance that Nature wants us here, that we are part of her plan.

Aluminum lily pads strung along the riverbank like beads invisibly connected to one another by beliefs. A Sunday blossoms into quenching peace, needs are fulfilled by rest, congregants celebrate the joy of doing nothing. Men compete for stillness, to see who can remain silent the longest, unwavering in their resolve to sit and just be one with the water until chance connects their hook to their fish, a treasured creature to be cradled gently in their hands, freed from the meanness of the barb, and released back into the deep, born again. It's a union of destinies. A fisherman can't fish without fish.

That morning cleansed me and refreshed my state of mind. I have been so immersed in the drama of the day, oblivious to my own need for respite and recalibration. Now I imagine the gods taking a day off from Armageddon to go fishing, and I want that feeling of release for myself. My survival demands it. I intend to make a religious ritual of doing nothing and perfect my practice.

I Could Be Wrong

XIII
GOOD
W
E
BAD
GURU

13. I Once Had a Sugar Daddy

I didn't spend much time thinking about cheating in marriage until I got cheated on, and then my self-righteousness mushroomed in thermonuclear rage. My husband died before we resolved our issues, and that made it easier to hold the point of view that I was all right and he was all wrong, until I had to pack up and move out of our house. Then I tripped over some forgotten stories about my own checkered past. When I was young, I had affairs with married men.

In 1975, my sugar daddy took me to a resort in Florida where he was supposed to be on a golf trip with his work buddies. I was 21 and he was in his mid 50s, married with a wife, two kids my age and a mother in a nursing home. He was Catholic and said he couldn't divorce his wife until his mother passed, because she would never forgive him. So, he and a group of colleagues from work rented a four-bedroom penthouse in New York City where they shacked up with their girlfriends — secretaries, waitresses, airline stewardesses and sex workers. They were suits with expense accounts, accustomed to three martini lunches, golf excursions during office hours, and business meetings over dinner in the evening. It wasn't difficult for them to come up with a story for their wives about why they wouldn't be home for supper with the kids.

Now I see these men as peers and I have a very different take on their behavior than I did when I was 21, waitressing without direction, broke in a big city where my sugar daddy became my safety net, my entertainment and my entrée to a lifestyle I could not afford. It didn't matter to me that he was married. I wasn't looking for love. I didn't give his wife a second thought. Her failed marriage was her problem. At the time, her husband was my carnival ride. I was with him just for the fun of it. His money lubricated our relationship. Our dates distracted me from the rough edges of my life, and I distracted him from his midlife crisis, a phrase that wasn't even in my vocabulary back then.

Perhaps we all go through a phase when our moral compass wobbles and we make the wrong choice. At 21, I never dreamed I would be on the receiving end of cheating in marriage. That was a failure of imagination. Cheating in marriage is quite common, but I was so arrogant I didn't think it would happen to me. Actually, I just didn't think about cheating, period. Having a doting sugar daddy padded my ego, insulating me from the anxiety of future betrayal.

We went to a cocktail party with his associates and their wives. The older women snubbed me in the powder room, rolled their eyes when I was introduced, put their backs to me to chat with each other, shunned me. I took it as a sign that I was winning, and they were losing. Instead of hurting my feelings, it sharpened my competitive edge. I was confident that I was at the top of my game, and they were simply old. Hmm... I have since learned that the arc of karma is long, and it bends toward payback.

I Could Be Wrong

IIII
MOTHER

14. Time is Not Money

For as long as I can remember we've been told time is money. But, of course, that's not true. If time were money, I'd be rich, because I have all the time in the world. Just to be sure, I checked my bank account. Yup. Time is definitely not money. Time is life.

I blame Ben Franklin for this bit of misinformation. In 1748, the early days of the Industrial Revolution, he wrote an article called "Advice to a Young Tradesman" saying, Remember that time is money, and admonishing workers that the way to build their wealth was to choose work instead of taking time to enjoy themselves doing other things. By Ben's lights, if workers weren't working, they weren't getting paid and they were losing money. That was before golf.

Now we know the time-is-money formula fails to factor in both the benefit of happiness (health and wellbeing, personal development, community building, productivity) and the cost of unhappiness (chronic illness, depression, anxiety, anger, violence, crime). Certainly, money has a relationship to happiness and unhappiness, but it's not the sole cause or cure. If money was all we need, the richest people in the richest country in the world would be the happiest people in the happiest country in the world — and we're not.

The United States ranks 19th on the current list of happiest countries in the world, and the countries that come before us on the list all have one thing in common. They're more generous than we are, better at sharing and spreading the wealth of their nation. According to the World Happiness Report, which is science, not opinion — math, not woowoo

— generosity is the defining characteristic of the happiest places on Earth.

Economists are measuring happiness because happiness actually has economic value. It's not that money doesn't matter. It's that the system for earning money has become so oppressive that it creates as many problems as it solves. Work should be a way of getting ahead, not falling behind. People who devote their lives to work without feeling a sense of progress drift into hopelessness, and that unhappiness has real economic costs, most particularly for healthcare and law enforcement. That's why happiness is the new buzzword in economics. Ben Franklin's formula for economic success valued the self-interest of greed over generosity. A better formula for success would be the Golden Rule. *Do unto others as you would have them do unto you.* Generosity is also motivated by self-interest.

A happy country, like a happy person, maintains a balance between greed and generosity. Is your life in balance? It's the season for evaluating ourselves and recalibrating our intentions. Consider generosity for a moment and see if you can work more of it into your plan. Remember, the happiest places are where people share the most. Share yourself, your home, your community, your humanity. Engage with the flesh and blood around you. Be generous. That's the way for all of us to build wealth for ourselves and each other.

I Could Be Wrong

IX
Flesh
Nugget
2/6
STAR

15. Professional Jealousy (Carnita #1)

Carnita was ambitious even as a fetus in her mother's womb when she absorbed her twin, surely destined to be a rival, and all her mother's other eggs, ensuring she would be an only child, a deliciously devious plan to have her own credit card by the time she was 12, and become a writer, a feminist writer to be precise, of the Virginia Woolf ilk, with her long wordy sentences and witty observations, if Virginia had written porn, because that was Carnita's ambition, to write feminist porn.

She was 15 the first time she had sex with a male, and the fiction of the pleasurable protuberance sent her into a revenge storm. Sex was not what it was cracked up to be. Explicit stories sprang up like psilocybin from her damp disappointment. Her inner feline strapped on claws, and she climbed out of the walled garden of girlhood into the dark crevasse of human nature, sticky fingers plucking sweet salty nuggets of flesh and pressing them into her keyboard, stroking, stroking, stroking, until the alphabet was exhausted, leaning back on one elbow, digging around her nightstand for a breath mint, accidentally belching the burp she had been holding in since that first kiss, before she was pushed down on the mattress, and gave control of her lady parts to a master.

She says she writes her best material in public, sitting with her laptop in coffee shops and diners, people-watching while mentally wrapped in the prickly legs of a lesser thinker, one who could never fully appreciate the nuance of her innuendo, her flippant verbology, the exquisite tension between her prime cut vocabulary and the lunch meat she was chopping at 200 words per minute. Carnita knew her audience too well to have any affection for them. Her readers were hungry puppies she occasionally kicked.

I admire a writer who is not beholden to likes. I ask myself, why am I not also a writer of erotica of the sort people pay for, and read aloud to their partner between the sheets and sleep? Carnita fluffs her keyboard on the table in front of her as I chew my bagel. Her fingers swarm in sassy prurience. Porn lubricates her mind, words pour out in frictionless acts, draining blood from brain to Neverland in blinding, liquid brilliance. Yes, I'm jealous. Why do I hesitate? Is it possible to injure your soul writing porn? Maybe I don't work hard enough.

As I question my legitimacy, she's on her third orgasm. Drips pool in dimples and curl around chins. I wonder what my friends will say when they discover I've started to write porn. Meanwhile Carnita's lead character ascends into heaven slurping oysters in an Italian sports car, careening down the Amalfi Coast, until she's on her last chapter, getting all Pulitzery, collapsing her lovers on the cliffs above the beach, carnal snacking sated, and I'm still sitting here, twisting a paper napkin around my flaccid ambition.

I Could Be Wrong

I
BABY DOLL

16. The Zen of Betsy Wetsy

In 1959 my parents, aka Santa Claus, gave me a baby doll for Christmas called Betsy Wetsy. I was an ecstatic five-year-old, and I kept her wrapped in her blanket until recently when I sold her for a couple bucks at a tag sale. Betsy Wetsy came with her own doll-sized baby bottle, and as you might infer from her name, she had one very special feature. She was a doll designed to simulate urination. Yes, Betsy Wetsy was designed to wet herself.

In the 1950s life was simple. There were only two genders, I was a girl, and girls became mothers. The Christmas I got Betsy Wetsy, my younger brother got a cowboy pistol and holster set. I'm sure my parents didn't think about toys as templates for skills or behavior. They were just happy to be giving us toys like the ones we saw on TV between the Mickey Mouse Club and the Howdy Doody Show.

If toys are templates for developing skills and behavior, what was the lesson I was supposed to learn from Betsy Wetsy? I was only five years old, but I knew she wasn't anatomically correct. The water in her baby bottle went in through a hole in her mouth and came out a hole in the side of her sweet little butt cheek. A potty-trained child knows that's not real.

How many times did I fill that baby bottle with water and put it in her mouth only to have the water leak out onto her clothes, her blanket and my lap? I don't remember, but I was a smart little kid. I'm sure it didn't take me long to learn that if the bottle was empty, Betsy wouldn't Wetsy on my dress. Was that the intended lesson? Don't feed the baby and you won't have to change its diapers. Probably not.

This is where the logic of the learned behavior and the intended lesson of the toy were dissonant.

Now I wish I could have been in the room when the toy company's Mad Men were talking about how to sell this new doll. Their pitch seems to have been that little girls should begin early to practice their mothering skills. In their minds the message of Betsy Wetsy was to be a good mommy. They didn't say, Imagine having three of these at the same time, and doing laundry, and fixing dinner for your husband. But they didn't have to. In that respect, Betsy Wetsy was quietly subversive.

I Could Be Wrong

VI
BITCH

17. Marlene

This is a true story about one of my most memorable mistakes. Marlene was probably twenty years older than me, but I didn't see it, and I didn't know what it meant. She was my idol. My goal was to have what she had, the corner office, the windows, the oriental rugs. She was at the top of her game. Men came to her for advice, favors, and that magic signature. She could sign off on anything and make it a reality. When the president came to speak, she was the one to manage him. Her people met with his people, they made spreadsheets and flow charts, and she nixed them all. Nothing was good enough for her. That's what made her so great. She could blow up an idea with one eyebrow.

I followed her for a year working on a special project. We traveled together and I got to see her prey on the account reps and sales guys who took her out to lunch and waited without complaining when she was an hour late. She wore Chanel suits and high heels, her lipstick was always perfect, and her hair was blond, that Jean Harlow blond that made her ageless. I never thought about how old she was because I thought she was beautiful. And she knew that. She played me into waiting on her hand and foot because she knew I worshipped her.

After a meeting of budget cuts and layoffs, she lit up one last cigarette to savor her dominion. Suits clustered around her like guppies. I'd point to my wristwatch to remind her we were late for our next meeting. If I stood too close to her, she blew smoke in my face. I should have known then she didn't respect me. But after a year as her assistant, I took it as a sign of affection.

I'd never worked with an older woman before, never really thought about aging. In my mind she was just like me. We were girls. Then one day she looked different to me, bigger, a lot bigger. Her skirt was like sandwich wrap. Her belly bulged over her hips. She came around and stood in front of her desk, leaning against it with her ankles crossed and her arms folded, and I had only one thought. It was the only thought I could have looking at her. My mind was flooded with a giddy anticipation.

"Oh, Marlene," I gushed. "You're pregnant. I'm so happy for you."

The look on her face was a bullet through my head and I knew I'd stepped in it.

"No," she snapped. "I'm not pregnant."

The next day I was transferred to a desk in the back of our distribution center. Never saw her again. Never understood. Until now.

I Could Be Wrong

XI
WIDOW

18. How to Process Grief

It has taken me a long time to learn how to process grief. So long in fact that I recently had the epiphany that certain kinds of grief may last forever. I realized I had been treating grief like a stain on my life that I could scrub away. But grief is part of my learned experience, my memories and my history, and that makes it part of my brain and my biology. I have a set of physical feelings of grief that creep over me when anniversaries come up. To learn how to process my grief I have to witness myself and consciously choose to think certain thoughts.

That deep longing for a loved one who is gone forever has its own biochemistry. When two bodies join in physical intimacy — lovers, life partners, a parent and child, a person and their dog — our microbiomes make connections, we swap bacteria, our scents are filled with microscopic messages of comfort, our neurotransmitters ping each other with the chemistry of joy. This is the biology of love. Love gives life purpose, pushes us to our limits, inspires hope for the future, and fulfills us. So, when we are suddenly cut off from the feelings, scents and signals of love, our brains go cold turkey into withdrawal and we experience emotional brain trauma, a lasting psychic injury, the biology of grief.

By the end of 2018, it was coming up on the tenth anniversary of my husband's death, and my bones seemed to know what time it was. But I didn't want to feel that sorrow again. I wanted to be done with it. I wanted to outgrow it. I thought my feelings were something my conscious mind could turn off. Instead, alone in my apartment ten years after the fact, I slid into murky sadness and felt awful in a very familiar way. That surprised me. I was disappointed in myself. I felt like I had failed to cure myself. What was wrong with me?

Now, a year later, I see that my ideas for how to process grief were mistaken. Grief is not a stain, a flaw or an imperfection. It's just another part of life, a permanent feature of my mind and body that may shrink or expand depending on my focus, but it's always there, and to be mentally healthy I have to learn to appreciate it. If love is unity, grief is loss, the flip side of love. The two come into our lives together, one the shadow of the other. To comfort myself I remember being loved and I try to love myself. I accept the emotional trauma of loss as core to my identity, I hug my dog, I talk to my friends, I go for a walk along the river, I listen to music, I meditate, I write, and I talk to myself. All of these positive activities dilute the negative brain chemistry of grief. I tell myself that I'm going to be okay, I'm fortunate to be here in this place with these tender memories, and I dwell in thankfulness for the love I've known.

I Could Be Wrong

VII
RAT

19. Cupidity

I recently had to look up the word "cupidity" and when I saw the definition, I was surprised that I didn't already know it. On sight, I assumed the word had something to do with Cupid, that plump little angel who pierces our hearts with arrows of love that trigger a craving for chocolate, cut flowers and Hallmark cards. But Cupid has a dark side — cupidity means greed. I went down the greed rabbit hole of search results, and I discovered there is a legitimate debate about whether greed is good or bad.

Then I had to look up legitimate, because who could possibly defend greed? Turns out economists, academics, Wall Streeters, and politicians think they have found the good in greed. In this case they are using the adult definition of good, as in adult films. You know, the kind of films we don't want children to see because a person does "good" by doing something that is technically wrong, like killing someone, or stealing from the rich to give to the less rich.

Reading about good greed and bad greed, I found a trove of other terms worth knowing. "Irrational exuberance" is when Wall Streeters get high at work and play fantasy football with your money. You can have the same feeling when you buy a ring at Target that looks exactly like a ring from Tiffany's. An "asset bubble" is like acid reflux for banks. They feel really full, but it's just gas coming from where the money should be.

When irrational exuberance leads to an asset bubble you get a recession. A recession is a correction, like when your parents sent you to bed without supper because you got caught lying. A global recession happens when the Wall Streeters high on irrational exuberance insure millions of rings from Target for the value of rings from Tiffany's, creating an asset bubble. Then they try to collect on millions of insurance policies, only to find a lot of smelly gas where the money should be. This is the bad kind of greed.

I did search for the good kind of greed, especially looking for a scenario that could make me feel better about taking too many napkins at the coffee shop. The words "Thou shalt not steal" were ringing in my head. Psychologists say greed is human nature, a survival instinct that's balanced by altruism. A cultural obsession with materialism can manifest greed as an allergy to satisfaction, making a person feel like they can never have enough. Today we call this allergy hoarding.

Some say when cave people tamed fire to cook, they were motivated by a fundamental greed for more food. Experts believe greed produced civilization. Greed for comfort produced chairs. Greed for convenience produced clocks. Greed for speed produced the wheel. If that's true, and I sure hope it is, maybe greed for good health will produce clean water. Because protecting water would definitely be the good kind of greed.

I Could Be Wrong

V
TEACHER

20. Vocabulary Lesson

I went to a medical appointment and I couldn't stop from wondering about the gender of the nurse's assistant who interviewed me and took my vitals. In my head I felt like I was being rude. But still my brain chugged through the list of typical traits for men and women, comparing them to the person who was taking my blood pressure. I wanted a pronoun as a label and a gender to box this person in. It's a habit, a way of seeing people, assigning them characteristics and predicting their behavior. He or she?

Gender has divided people into two groups my whole life. Until now. Now gender seems fluid, less confining, a choice. At least, I'm learning to see it that way. In the 1970s I went to a public high school where females weren't allowed to wear pants and males weren't allowed to wear long hair. Back then nurses wore white dresses with little white hats and nylon stockings. I was boxed in as a girl the day I was born. I marched in the streets for women's rights. Biology is not destiny. Yet part of my brain wants to box in the nurse's assistant.

Driving through the city I saw a thin young woman with a messy bun standing on the street corner, and I had the thought that if I grew my hair out, I would wear a messy bun like hers. Then she crossed the street in front of me and I saw she had a full beard. She was a he. Man bun. Presumably. Gender is an assumption.

At the grocery store the cashier was a young man with long shining black hair in jeans and a t-shirt, and full Kardashian makeup, boomerang eyebrows chiseled into caramel skin, glittering purple lids, butterfly lashes, contoured cheekbones and glossy lips. He was beautiful. I told him so and he flashed a brilliant smile. So why am I calling him a he? Intuition, I guess. I think it was the t-shirt. But, of course, I don't know.

My barista is a young person with dark facial hair and a wispy mustache in a spaghetti-strap sundress, wearing a pair of fabulous vintage earrings. I want those earrings. So, I ask if they're pierced or clip-ons, do they hurt their ears, how old are they? After scouring them for clues, the person, not the earrings, I give up on the gender checkbox. I see my curiosity is reflexive. This person doesn't fit the gender template in my mind. But gender is not a template.

"Where's the ladies' room?" The words come out of my mouth without a thought. On the door it says All Gender Restroom. I remember the days of the Miss, Mrs., Ms. fight. I checked the Ms. box because I wanted the right to define myself. Now the principle of un-gendering my pronouns seems similar. People have the right to define themselves. They, them, their. Words matter. It's going to take me a while, but I get it.

I Could Be Wrong

I
Hand Cream
WATCHDOG

21. Hand Cream

This morning I woke and stretched against my pillows, looked up at my arms and saw my grandmother's skin. I remember when I was a girl looking at the papery tissue of her arms and the deep grooves in her hands, and thinking she needed to use more hand cream. Of course, now I know that hand cream isn't going to stop my skin from becoming parchment. Parchment is my destiny. But a plan could help me feel okay about that.

I have had the urge lately to make a plan, a big important master plan that will be my to-do list for the next decade, a yardstick against which I'll measure myself and keep my life on track. Having a plan would make me feel better about not knowing what I'm doing because it would look like I do know what I'm doing, and whenever I doubt myself, all I have to do is look at the plan. See? No doubt. There's a plan. I definitely know what I'm doing.

When I'm feeling uncertain about my future, I open Excel and start making spreadsheets, high tech grids I deploy to manage all the important issues in my life. I'm not putting my faith in some goop that comes in a fancy jar with slick advertising. I'm putting my faith in a software program that sorts information into little boxes, in a vast hive of boxes that can be converted into a pie chart. Organizing myself into rows and columns makes me feel in control. We all have our tricks for coping.

Age is climbing up on me like kudzu, and I feel like I need a plan for what to do with it. In my 20s I had a plan to manage rock bands in the music business and become rich and famous. That didn't work. In my 30s I had a plan to conquer a desk job and claw my way to the top. Did okay with that. In my 40s I had a plan to develop a software company and own it. Almost did that. In my 50s I had a plan to be a farmer and make a living from my farm. Complete disaster. Although I loved it. Now I'm in my 60s, single in the city, drifting through my days, yacking up the alphabet, using Facebook as a megaphone. And a little voice inside me keeps asking, what's the plan?

I have to remind myself that having a plan never gave me control over my life. But it would make me feel good to have my future plotted on a grid from now until I'm 90. Little boxes of text would give me comfort that I'm going to be okay. Then the sun shines in my window and the day spreads out before me as virgin territory, and I ask myself — Shall I crack open a spreadsheet and angst over my long game, or should I just go out and buy some hand cream?

I Could Be Wrong

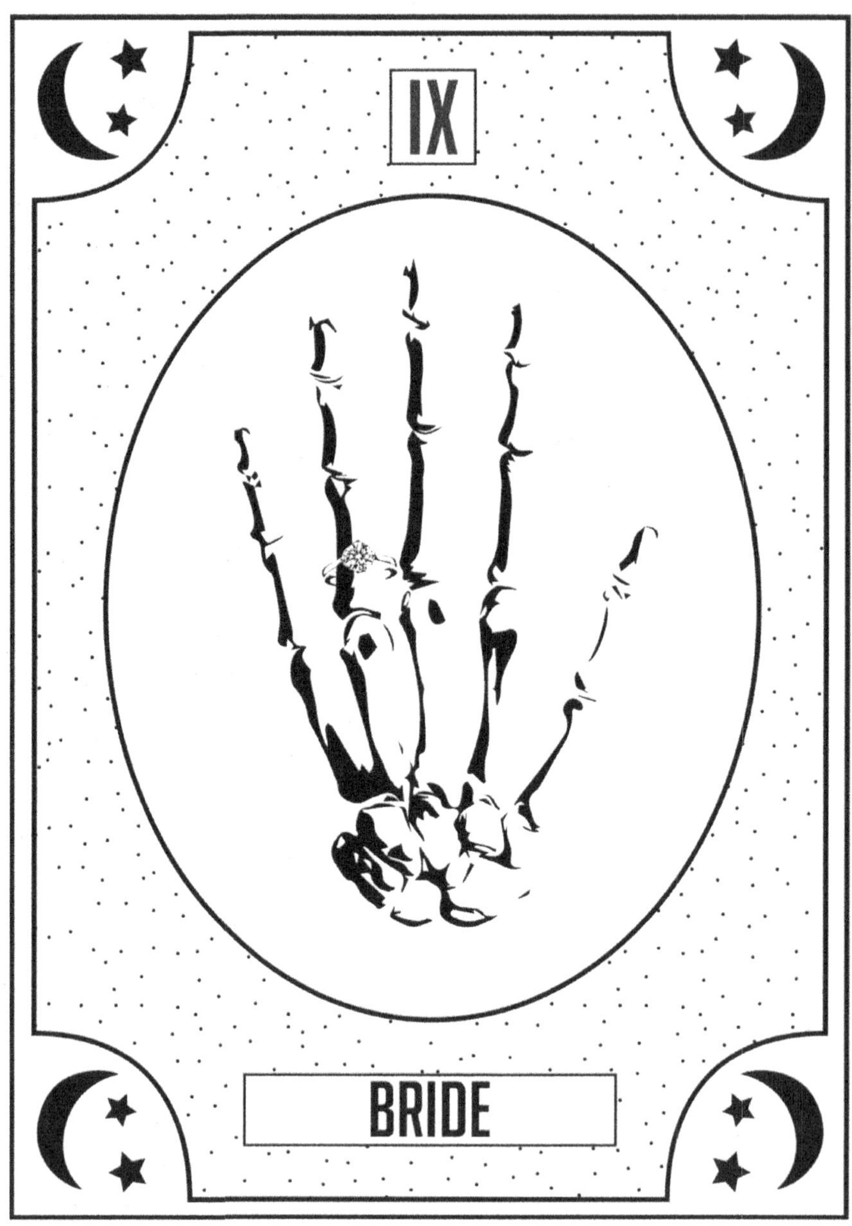
IX
BRIDE

22. Plan Death Like a Wedding

When my husband realized he had only a few months to live he told me he thought we should plan his death like a wedding because it was just as important. Yes, I was surprised. It was 2008. I hadn't considered planning death, and it seemed radical to plan death like a wedding. I thought we would just let it roll and I would somehow cope. But he had a vision for what he wanted, and I soon realized it was based on the way his dad died.

My father-in-law refused to plan his death or acknowledge that he was dying, even when he was in hospice. That refusal left the family leaderless, and instead of focusing on the profound aspects of the experience, they got all tangled up in feuding over the details, like yellow roses or white? Should he be buried wearing his Army dog tags and his rings, or not? Which pair of cowboy boots should he wear? Who got to ride in the limousine? It all seems petty now, but at the time these were the issues that gripped my mother-in-law and her family in all-out war over who was in charge of this event. Instead of Bridezilla, think Widowzilla. And she wasn't even a widow yet.

When my husband got the diagnosis of terminal cancer, the first thing he said was, I'm not going to die the way my father did, and he began to plan his death. He was a musician and he understood death as his final performance. He enrolled himself in hospice and met with a palliative care physician. Then he announced I was forbidden to dial 911, no matter what happened. Then he told me he wanted his body to be kept wherever he died for 24 hours, not moved, and handled only by people who loved him, me and his friends. He wanted to be wrapped in white linen for cremation, as he imagined Ghandi may have been. Thankfully not in his purple spandex stage pants. And he wanted his ashes spread on our farm.

That was eleven years ago, and today I see how fortunate I was to be caring for a man who wanted to plan his death as a ceremonial event like a wedding. He was the leader of the process, he was conscious of his impact on the living, and he was curious. He died quietly on a bed in our livingroom and the next day I invited friends to come visit him. They brought flowers, gathered around his body, told stories and listened to music. It was just how he wanted it to be.

Now I'm thinking ahead for myself, considering my age and the unpredictability of life, and I want to plan my death like a wedding, too. I want the gathering of friends, the flowers, the stories and the music. You're invited. I hope together we can create a serene experience that celebrates the flow of life, the reunion of death and our unbroken bond to Nature. And, one more thing. I would like people to laugh. Laughing at all that has transpired here is key to finding peace. I'll be listening from somewhere, and I'd like to hear your laughter. Thanks.

I Could Be Wrong

VIII
LOVER

23. Girl with the Far Away Eyes

It was obvious to me that she could never love him the way he loved her. But he wouldn't listen. He was obsessed with her. That was the crazy thing about their relationship. It was completely out of balance. She had all the power. He made a fool of himself following her, waiting for her to make eye contact and give him a sign that she felt the way he did. But she kept him in the friend zone.

They met on one of those vacations when you're looking for something, but you don't really know what it is. She caught his attention on the veranda as they stared out at the lake. Her far away eyes pulled him in, and from that moment she was all he could think about. On the beach, strolling through the gardens, wandering the grounds of the hotel, he searched for her, hoping she wanted what he wanted, wishing for the impossible.

But it wasn't meant to be. She was a high-class dame, out of reach for a guy like him; a mixed-up redhead, part lover, part killer, all diva. And she was smart, so smart sometimes he was afraid of her. She threw him off his game. When he found her alone on the lawn, her scent intoxicated him, and she knew it. She teased him, danced him in circles until she felt his hot breath on her neck. Then suddenly, she just walked away and left him standing there. She was ruthless.

I took him for a drive around the lake and tried to talk some sense into him. But he just wanted to get back to the hotel. I told him she wasn't the right kind of girl, but he didn't care. She was a drug and he was begging for it. I wanted to be angry, but I understood. Once in a lifetime love comes along and sweeps you away with one look. You can't explain it, but in your heart you know. Everything you thought was important slips away — your stick, your tennis ball, your desiccated liver treats. Squirrels recede into the background, meaningless. You forget about the Frisbee under the bed.

It was a long week. We watched fiery sunsets and listened to night birds call across the lake. But in his mind, he was always with her. She was the chew toy buried in the couch, the gopher in the stone wall, the pigeon on the sidewalk. I could see the yearning in his eyes, that wild lust for an unattainable fantasy. He watched her through the window as we drove away for the last time, and I knew he would never be the same. Love changed him. She was out of sight, but she was alive his dreams like a picnic ham on a blanket in the park.

I Could Be Wrong

IV
GRANDMA

24. In the Time of Chairs

I've often wanted to live in a simpler time with less stuff, less pressure and less noise, cooking slow food by firelight, living in a cave with everyone I know eating together and sleeping together. Just kidding. If I was going to travel back in time, I wouldn't go back before the time of chairs. I really like chairs. And I'm not so sure about everyone sleeping in one room. The snores must have been deafening. I come from a family of snorers. In a cave, the echo of my mother's snore could have started a rockslide.

Of course, if I lived in cave times, I would be the oldest woman alive. Back then women became grandmothers in their 30s and almost no one lived past 40. Grandmothers helped their adult daughters who were pregnant, rocking a new baby and breastfeeding a toddler, all at the same time. There was no planned parenthood. So, grandmothers had an important role to play in managing the children and teaching them how to find food.

A grandmother took the kids and walked to the nearest watering hole, got down on her hands and knees, and drank. Maybe she filled an animal bladder with water to carry back to the cave. Then she taught the kids to identify edible plants and dig for tubers, those nutritious roots that enabled cave people to carbo-load. On her hands and knees in the dirt, she foraged with a stick and took the tubers back home where she collected wood to build a fire and roast them in the hot coals. Then, still on her hands and knees, she fed her family. Imagine grocery shopping on your hands and knees, walking home, and making dinner on your kitchen floor. My knees hurt just thinking about it.

Back then a grandmother's role was to share her wisdom to ensure the survival of her family. Daily life was an extreme sport and her age was a testament to her skills. She was valued for her knowledge, but her rugged existence abbreviated her lifespan. I'm so glad I don't have to crawl around on my hands and knees and eat weeds to prove I'm worthy. A chair may seem to be the simplest of objects, but chairs got us up off the floor so we could live long enough to have joint replacement surgery. They elevated Cleopatra to sit on her throne and rule Egypt, Mary Shelley to sit at her desk and write *Frankenstein*, Aretha Franklin to sit at her piano and demand respect, and me — I'm just thankful I don't to have carve my blog posts on stone tablets.

So next time you have a seat, lean back and put your elbows on the armrests, feel your good fortune and have a moment of gratitude for the ten-thousand-thousand grandmothers who worked a lifetime on their hands and knees so we could take it easy living in the time of chairs.

I Could Be Wrong

II
FREE THE NIPPLE
SUFFRAGETTE

25. Free the Nipple

It's spring and people on the street are showing their skin. Some more than others. Women are letting the sunshine on their cleavage and young men are jogging bare-chested along the river. How exhilarating it must be to feel the fresh air moving across your skin as you run half-naked without fear of arrest or assault.

When I went to Macy's to buy a bra, I commented to the sales associate about how most of the bras had some kind of thick padding, which I assumed was to exaggerate a woman's amplitude. She informed me that the padding was not about enlargement, it was about hiding nipples. She said, "Imagine what it would be like to stand in front of a classroom of kids or a meeting of office people and have your nipples go erect. Suddenly everyone is staring at your nipples."

Well, I can imagine that. In the 1970s, I was one of those women who burned my bra and declared myself free of that sexist entrapment. At the time, we called that going native, and it was a sign of women's liberation. But about ten years later, I willingly strapped one on because I wanted to look professional. To dress for corporate success, nipples need not apply.

Now, I'm blessed with a mammalian abundance that makes going native uncomfortable. I wouldn't dream of running anywhere without my breasts contained, lest I find myself in the emergency room trying to explain how I broke my own jaw. Today I can be liberated and harnessed. But even so, I'd like to have the right to run bare-chested down the street. I'd like to know what it feels like to be unafraid of going bare-chested in public the way men do.

Portland has a naked bike ride once a year and thousands of naked bicycle riders participate. The ride is permitted by the city, although the starting place and route are announced only at the last minute so the public cannot line the streets to watch, and participants can feel safe. The rules are don't gawk, don't touch, don't photograph, don't comment. Still, you won't find me flopping around Portland on a bicycle with the twins.

Going naked in public is not my idea of fun, but it is my idea of freedom. It may not be practical or hygienic. All sorts of icky images come to mind. So, I'm not advocating for the right to show up naked at Chipotle and spill hot sauce on my pubes. No shirt, no shoes, no service. I'm fine with that. But when I see a guy running down the street wearing nothing but his jogging shorts and shoes, or on the beach in what for me would be only half a swimsuit, I can't help but feel a little jealous that he has a freedom I've never had, even though we are supposedly equal.

I Could Be Wrong

X
PILOT

26. Solo Flight (Senior and Single)

When I was a teenager, inspired by Twiggy and Cher, my friends and I rolled up our skirts to make them shorter and put on make-up in the restroom at school where our mothers couldn't see us. Lined up in front of those sinks and mirrors, we ratted our hair into bouffants, padded our bras with our socks, critiqued our changing bodies, and gossiped.

Boy crazy was a phrase we used to describe a girl judged to be delirious with the desire to be part of a couple. All the cool girls had boyfriends. The coolest girls broke up with one boyfriend to start up with a better one. Girls were measured by their boyfriend's status and success. That's how it's always been.

Now I'm 65, and it's a rush to witness all those body changes all over again — shape, skin, face, hormones, hair. And I still follow the latest fashions, even if I don't wear them. But one thing is quite different in my late life metamorphosis. I'm not boy crazy. Since puberty I was either looking for a man or I had one. But being part of a couple doesn't interest me anymore. It's no longer a driving force in my life. That's a big change for me.

For 32 years of marriage my life was organized around another person. It took me years after my husband died to learn to live alone. There was no dress rehearsal for being single. Suddenly my co-pilot was gone, and I was flying solo. Then once I got comfortable with my circumstances, I had to face other people thinking that I wasn't whole if I didn't have a husband, that I couldn't possibly be happy, that it was risky. You'd be surprised how many people think a woman's life purpose is to be the accompaniment to a man.

I'm not looking for a partner because for the first time in my life, I have the freedom to focus on myself. In this next phase I want to concentrate on my own talents and ingenuity. I want to explore new dreams. Elder women are a powerful force for change in the world. We have the will, the wisdom, and the resources to tilt humanity toward wellbeing. That excites me. I want to be part of that.

I have my moments of anxiety just like everybody else. But I push through them because I believe in my future. I don't want to be somebody else. I'm living with my dog in a one-woman nest, looking forward to a new set of achievements, and I'm thrilled by the possibilities. My life is finally all about me, and it feels like a gift.

I Could Be Wrong

XI
BOUNCER

27. My Ugly Shoes

I get spooked when my hips and knees hurt. I'm trying to make it through this life with all my original equipment. Joint pain is one of the reasons I stopped farming, sold my house, and moved into a much smaller place. The physical labor of farming was grinding my bones together. I did it for love, so no complaints. But it was obvious to me that I couldn't continue unless I planned on having my joints replaced.

I lived on my farm for 18 years and the whole time I wore muck boots outside. But they weren't my favorite shoes. When I got dressed up to go into town, I wore leather street shoes. After I moved to the city and began walking my dog on the sidewalk, I wore my leather street shoes everyday strolling for miles on cement, and it wasn't long before my knees and my hips started hurting again. A friend suggested I change my shoes from thin soles to something with more bounce. That was a disappointment. There was a reason other than manure that I never owned athletic shoes. I thought they were ugly.

Researching my problem, I made a mind-boggling discovery. Yes, my feet are changing. They started out cushioned with a layer of thick spongy fat, like deep dish pizza dough. Now they're cushioned by a thin delicate layer of fat, like a French crepe. That's why my bones have no bounce. My foot fat is disappearing. Really? The fat on the bottom of my feet has disappeared all on its own? Without me even knowing it was there? That kills me.

If walking on my feet for 65 years is all it takes to make my layer of foot fat disappear, maybe I should have been rolling around on the floor for a few hours every day to lose all that other fat. It doesn't seem fair that the only fat that disappears with age is the fat no one could see in the first place. Maybe my foot fat didn't disappear at all — maybe it just crawled up my leg to my thighs.

Eventually I got a pair of high-tech athletic shoes. They're like tire tread with laces. But their soles absorb the impact of the sidewalk, they insulate my joints from the repetitive jolt, and the traction protects me from slipping and sliding. The pain in my knees and my hips has subsided. So, I've succumbed to ugly shoes. Really ugly shoes. At least until I find a way to suck the fat out of my thighs and put it back on the bottom of my feet where it belongs.

I Could Be Wrong

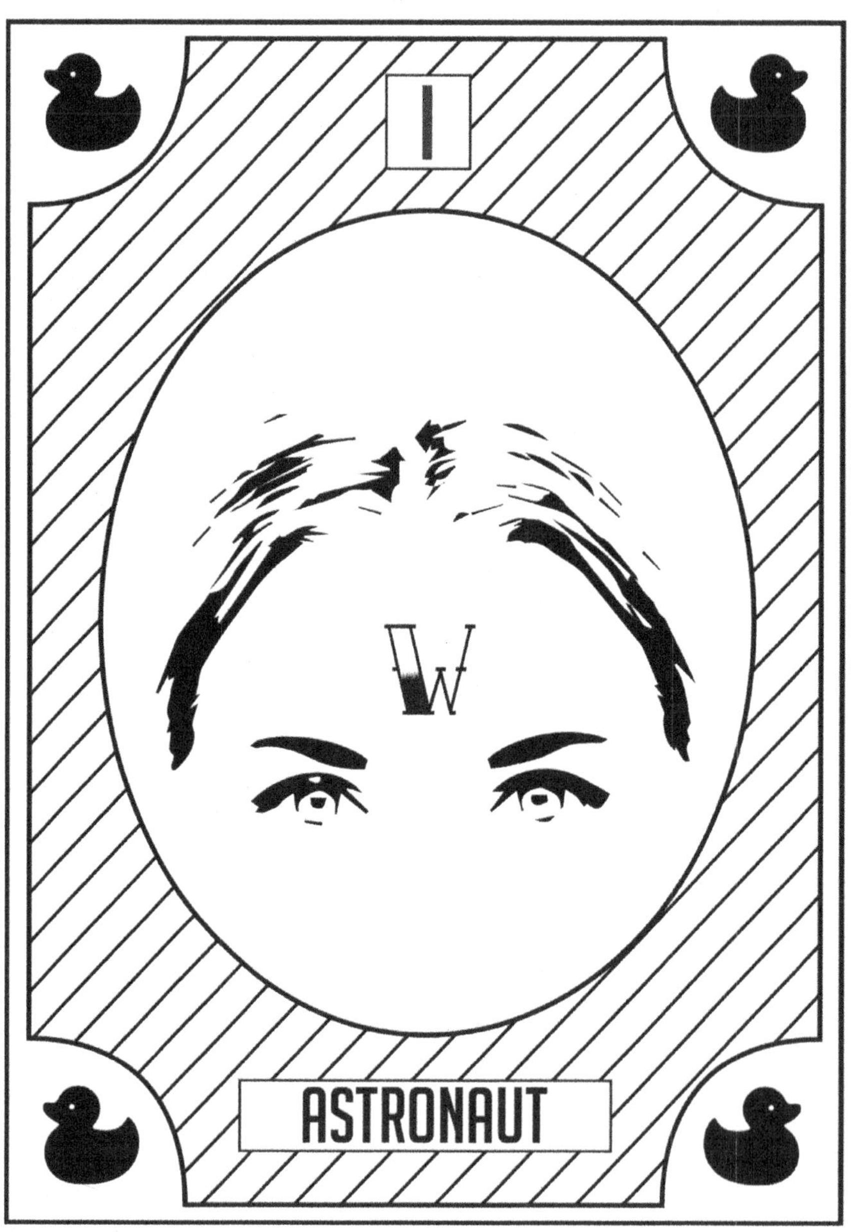
I
W
ASTRONAUT

28. How to Move Forward After Becoming a Widow

It took me years to figure out how to move forward after becoming a widow. That word felt like a black letter W tattooed on my forehead, a title conferred upon me without my consent. It seemed to me that being a widow was a lower social caste than being married. It was a pity card that came with its own set of patronizing facial expressions and a tone of voice that said your ticket has been downgraded. "I'm sorry. You no longer have a seat in first class." It was bad enough that I had lost my husband, but then I felt as though social norms were suddenly different for me, as though I was defective. Expectations for my future were diminished. It was a wave of new feelings entwined with my grief. I was angry.

The history of widows is bleak. Since biblical times they have been mistreated, enslaved, stripped of their social status, forced to give up their possessions and sometimes even forced to give up their children. They have been married off to their husband's brothers and forced to become breeders for his family. In Egyptian lore a widow could be buried alive in her husband's tomb. In India a widow could be burned alive on her husband's funeral pyre. In Nepal widows could be forbidden to wear red because red is the color of joy. Even in the U.S. a widow could lose her land and her house, her retirement funds, her credit cards and her cable service. A widow is expected to cancel her plans for the future.

Now time has given me some perspective on how to move forward after becoming a widow. It's been eleven years and I'm not saddled with that awful word anymore. I live in a new place where no one knows my history. It's a fresh start. I see the widow label as an example of structural sexism, a gender trap set by the patriarchy. What do we call men whose wives die? Widower. The grammatical form of the word says it all. A man is expected to shake off his loss and hook up again. I know, history is complicated, and social norms are no one's fault. We can't blame the other gender for our lives. But you do see the difference between being a widow and being a widower, right? Men don't get burned alive or forbidden to wear the color of joy.

There is one other significant difference between widows and widowers — often women who have the means to survive on their own choose not to hook-up again. After a life of caregiving for family, many women find freedom in suddenly being single, even with their grief. This isn't a commentary on love or the quality of marriage. I loved my husband. But now that I've learned how to move forward after becoming a widow, I'm not turning back, not signing up to be a caregiver again, not yearning to be part of a twosome. My life is my own and I'm celebrating my independence, wearing the color of joy and making plans for the future.

I Could Be Wrong

V
JUNKIE

29. True Confessions

Have you ever been addicted? I started smoking in 1967 when I was 13. My friend's parents smoked Winstons, and they bought them by the carton, so they didn't notice when a pack went missing. The ashtray on their kitchen table was always dirty, and there were cigarette butts in every wastebasket in the house, so they didn't smell our smoke when they came home from work. In the hour between the end of school and the time they arrived, we crowded into their kitchen and sucked burned tobacco into our lungs.

Then I got my driver's license and it became easy to buy cigarettes, because cigarette machines were everywhere, and a pack cost only 50 cents. Winston, Salem, Marlboro, Lucky Strike, Pall Mall, Newport, Camel, Viceroy, Kent and Kool, all in a row. Ashtrays invited smokers to light up in restaurants, hotel lobbies, hospitals, bus stations and airports, even on airplanes. Every car came with an ashtray and a cigarette lighter. Smoking wasn't just accepted, it was encouraged.

Each cigarette brand had a distinct taste, the taste became part of the habit, and I always had a favorite brand. Advertising for cigarettes was ubiquitous on TV, billboards, magazines, and radio. Every brand had a slogan and a jingle. Cigarettes were pop culture, changing with the times. One brand in particular, Virginia Slims, targeted the women's liberation movement with the slogan, You've come a long way baby. The last brand I smoked was Natural American Spirit, because, you know, natural is healthier.

At the peak of my habit I went through two packs a day. I did try to quit several times, but my friends smoked, colleagues at the office smoked, my in-laws smoked, people smoked in public places, in restaurants, nightclubs and bars. My husband smoked pot. There was no escape from smoke. Everywhere I went I was surrounded by the sight of others taking long draws on those lit sticks, getting buzzed.

It wasn't until I started farming in 2003 that I finally kicked the habit. Cigarettes and hay are a lethal combination, and I really, really wanted cows. I promised myself when I became a farmer that I would quit smoking. By then I could hold a cigarette between my lips while I sat in the lotus position, so I could smoke and do yoga at the same time.

That's addiction for you. I had to experience it to understand it. Even after all these years of abstinence, cigarettes come to me in dreams and whisper their promises. In fact, just yesterday I was walking past a guy on the sidewalk as he lit up, and it smelled amazing, and I had that passing thought. Just one. I'll have just one...

I Could Be Wrong

XIII
TRICKSTER

30. Click This

I walk my dog along the Willamette River where fishermen drop their lines in the water from dawn to dusk, playing catch-and-release with the sturgeon that swim there. The fishermen use a bait of chopped herring they call chum. Their chum often dribbles onto the ground around them, and they leave it where it falls on the wharf, because it isn't worth the effort to pick it up. I wouldn't even know it was there if my dog wasn't so attracted to the stinky bits.

Now chum has taken on new meaning as the term for a particular type of online advertising, and it's a very fitting descriptor. You've probably seen a photograph of a medicine bottle with the headline "The Secret Pill Billionaires Are Taking," or a picture of something icky with the headline "10 Signs You Have A Tapeworm," or a wrinkled woman with the headline "She Had Sex On Her 100th Birthday." That's chum. Often several of these images are arranged on a grid called a chumbox.

Of course, I want to read these stories. If the richest people in the world are all taking the same pill, maybe I should be taking it, too. A tapeworm would explain my incessant craving for a bacon cheeseburger. And I want to see a picture of the person a 100-year-old babe had sex with, assuming it wasn't herself.

Unfortunately, there's no story behind these headlines. Chum is bait for advertising, not information. A chumbox is delivered to a website by a software company that promotes itself as a "content discovery" service. Right. Chum is content like the stinky bits of dead fish on the wharf are food. The content in a chumbox will lead you straight to the internet's waste matter.

I could lose an hour trying to figure out if that mother bear really hugged the guy who saved her cub from drowning, and I get a secret satisfaction out of knowing how "These Celebrity Facelifts Ruined Their Careers." I should have chum controls on my browser with a pop-up box that warns, "Don't You Have Something Better to Do?"

Chum could turn my brain to mush the way it gives my dog the Hershey squirts. But chum is big business. Billions of dollars are being made by spreading mind pollution on the internet. It's a cynical strategy and it works. It works because when I read "Ice Cream Facial Proven to Reverse Aging" I want to know what flavor ice cream. Do you have to melt it first? Can I use frozen yogurt instead?

See what I mean? I've learned to steer my dog away from the wharf when the fishermen are out there with their chum buckets. But it takes more discipline to steer myself away from chum online. No one sweeps the sidewalks or takes out the trash on the internet. It's up to me to step around it.

I Could Be Wrong

IX
DINNER
WIFE

31. Queen of the House

My mother-in-law, Mary Evelyn, had the coolest retro kitchen with bright red linoleum countertops, a big enamel sink, and a 1950's stove with curvy lines and big plastic knobs. It was always perfectly clean and tidy because she had a secret method for cleaning her kitchen — she refused to cook. She grew up in the 1930s and 40s when a woman was expected to slog over a hot stove. Then she discovered canned soup.

On holidays she ordered a ham and potato salad from the deli. Weeknight dinners were usually self-serve. She lived on cheese and crackers and diet soda. Every once in a while, she had a burst of culinary inspiration and made her special Bologna Ring, which was pink sausage boiled with canned string beans.

I learned a lot from her, but not about cooking, about setting boundaries. Once she sat down on the couch there was no moving her. She felt no obligation to wait on her family. She watched her mother slave her life away raising chickens, baking bread, and sewing clothes for her children. No way was Mary Evelyn going to do that.

On summer mornings she sat on her porch swing in her nightgown and rocked in the shade. If she was feeling ambitious, she might get a bottle of weed killer out of the garage. Then barefoot, with a cigarette in one hand and the squirt bottle in the other, she'd walk up and down the driveway and the sidewalk, squirting poison on anything green that dared poke up from the cracks in the cement.

If my father-in-law happened to see her through the kitchen window, while he made his morning Sanka with hot tap water and drank it over the sink, he would yell at her through the window screen, "Mary, get in here and put some damn clothes on. You look like a damn hillbilly out there in your damn nightgown." And she would yell back at him, "Oh, Maurice, shut up. You'll wake the neighbors."

Mary Evelyn was solidly middle class and intentionally uneducated. She didn't want to learn anything new. Her main interests were sports and shopping for things on sale. Her basement shelves were lined with incredible deals she got on baked beans and tuna fish, paper towels and plastic cups. She stockpiled rows and rows of canned food in case there was another Depression or a war shortage.

Her whole family tried to change her, but her ways were set, and trying to talk to her about her unhealthy diet, or the expiration date on the cans in the basement, could get your eardrums blown out by a sudden increase in volume on the TV. Mary Evelyn didn't want to change. It was just that simple. She got married, had kids, kept a nice house, and made sure there was always plenty of lunch meat in the fridge for her husband. After that, she was entitled to do whatever she pleased.

I Could Be Wrong

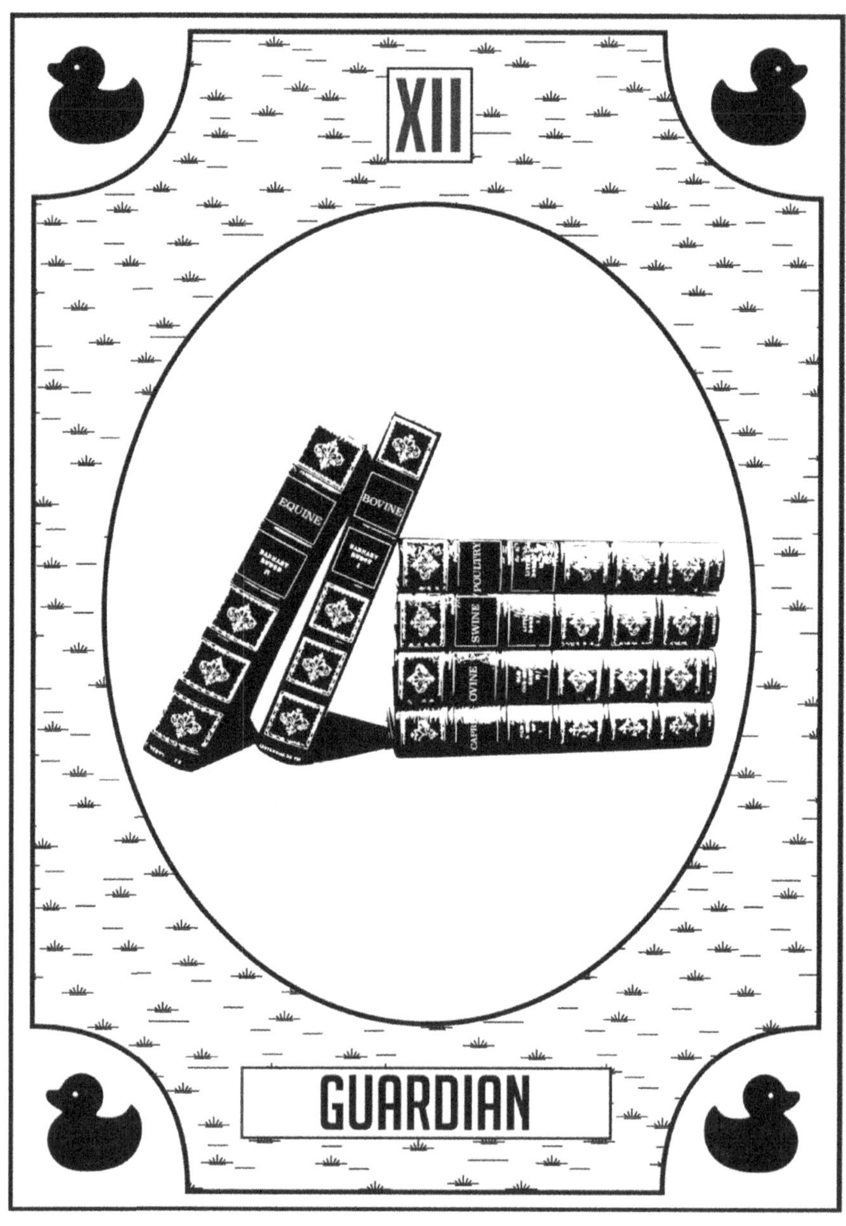
XII
EQUINE
BOVINE
POULTRY
SWINE
OVINE
GUARDIAN

32. Thinking Off the Grid

I once read an encyclopedia on farm animals. It was like that scene in the Matrix when Trinity is escaping on the stolen helicopter, a machine she has never flown, and just as she takes the pilot seat the instructions for how to fly that helicopter are downloaded from the mothership to the memory chip installed behind her ear. Without skipping a beat, the woman's hands begin to move across the controls and her iron bird lifts off from the rooftop of a skyscraper. I was thinking reading an encyclopedia on farming would be just like that. So, I read "The Encyclopedia of Historic and Endangered Livestock and Poultry Breeds" from cover to cover.

Books are my key to the Universe. I read and do, read and do, read and do, until finally I'm certain I know, and I don't need to learn anymore. I just do. Often that's when I make my biggest mistakes. I'm so certain of what I know that I don't allow for the possibility of learning something new. My knowledge becomes a series of switches, on/off, yes/no, right/left, open/closed, a grid of pre-existing ideas that becomes a filter for everything that enters my mind.

Thinking on that grid extrudes new information so it looks a lot like the old information and my thoughts become a pattern that repeats itself in my behavior until parts of my grid are so worn from overuse that they become deep ruts, and I bury myself in certainty until my grid is shattered by my own humiliating ignorance. My failure to learn new information and change my behavior often leaves me in a mess. For me, farming was a process of correcting my mistakes as fast as I could discover them.

A farm is not a machine. I thought educating myself with words would be like downloading the farm chip. But, of course, living things are always changing and adapting, coming together and falling apart, shedding their skin, losing their feathers, sprouting seeds, procreating, hatching and diversifying. The job of farming is to manage diversity and keep life flowing in one direction, which is impossible. That's why they call it work. Life is a river, not a grid. The world flows toward chaos.

I amused myself looking at cow porn and bought expensive bull semen online, but the artificial insemination failed and after a year of trying to get my cows pregnant with human hands, I finally got a real bull. I discovered my carelessness with chicken feed was an invitation to rats, which invaded the farm unnoticed until I found one in the house. I thought I would be able to shear sheep by watching a guy at the fair, and trim goats' hooves by looking at pictures, but my hand muscles were uncooperative. There was no chip I could download with the muscle memory of farming.

I thought I could crawl under an electric fence on wet grass in the rain, forgetting that the water on my clothes would conduct electricity. The shock was so bad I let out an involuntary scream and wet my pants. There's no chip for instinct. I learned that it's not always smart to be brave, and sometimes it's faster to slow down. As much as I'd like to keep my life simple and believe easy answers, I know I have blind spots. My next big mistake is flowing toward me right now and seeing with an open mind is my best defense.

I Could Be Wrong

VII
ED
TEENAGER

33. Good Girl, Bad Girl

I wrote my boyfriend's name on my stomach with masking tape and laid in the sun until I was burned. Then I peeled the tape off and there it was in bold caps — ED. It was the high point of my summer. I was 13, it was 1968, and no one had ever told me to stay out of the sun. Sun tans were cool, the souvenir of summer. Burning Ed's name into my abdomen was the equivalent of getting a tattoo, just short of being engaged, a symbol of eternal love, a willingness to be owned by a relationship.

Ed was the older brother of a really cute guy I liked better. But the cute guy didn't like me. So, I flirted with Ed. They were from an Italian family, exotic people with black hair in white bread Illinois, swarthy boys with square shoulders who shaved before the others, and made wise cracks, and worked at the gas station. At 13, having a boyfriend with whiskers and a job was status. Ed was a man.

In our town there were good girls and bad girls. Riding my bicycle to the gas station to gawk at Ed was a first step toward being a bad girl. My mother would have been furious, but she never knew. Not about the sunburned letters under my shirt, not about my fizzy daydreams of Ed, not about me standing around the gas station with my babysitting money, buying a Babe Ruth candy bar from the vending machine and eating it one tiny bite at a time so I could have an excuse talk to him.

I remember the feeling of floating in that greasy room with the stained cement floor, shelves lined with motor oil, a paper towel dispenser on the wall behind the cash drawer, a jar of pens and a tablet of blank receipts on the linoleum countertop. Ed wiped his hands on his pants in black fingers of oil and gasoline. His sweat sparkled. In the mind of a 13-year-old girl trapped with her family in a ranch house on a dead-end gravel road, Ed was excitement, defiance of the cookie cutter I was pressed into by my parents, my church, my school, my town.

Of course, I wish I could have explained to my 13-year-old self that the shimmering mirage of Ed and me had no substance, that pairing up, two by two, was not the goal in life. I can hear myself now droning on about achievement, ambition and independence, until my 13-year-old eyes glaze over, and my 13-year-old feet start inching toward the screen door. "There are other things in life besides boys," I say to her.

"I know," she says in a two-note chirp. "I'm going for a bike ride." And off she flies, alone, hair in the wind, eyes on the horizon, skin burning in the sun.

I Could Be Wrong

V
STALKER

34. The Cooking Lesson (Carnita #2)

I've been stalking Carnita because she's practically famous for her new porn travelogue and it kills me. How can a writer care nothing for sentence structure? She doesn't even proofread her work. But still she sells a steady stream of words ejaculated onto the page, while I agonize and judge. Her alphabet isn't the same as mine. My fingers dry up clumsy above the keyboard while letters cream out of her, each story a lubricant sucked up by her audience, morsels of lust consumed one page at a time. Do I have to be graphic to be successful? Is metaphor lost to the modern mind? Wherefore art thou poetry? Porn feels like the writing End Times to me, but for Carnita its all Rapture. These are the things I'm thinking about while she plans her book tour.

First stop Germany where she will eat meat. She's never been much of a meat eater. Meat could change her, give her some kind of insatiable craving, keep her awake at night. After a year of pinning wings on mermaids, she's planning to surprise her fans with bratwurst and the erection of Eltz Castle, sharp spires poking through the canopy in a fairytale piercing of the musk and fur of the forest. The cooking lesson was her dress rehearsal, a precious whisper of instructions, ingredients artfully arrayed on a marble table, nostrils splayed by the viscous scent, long muscles fermented dark beside pink mounds of flesh. Her fingers wander instinctively, fire dancing through pheromones of the ancients, swans entwined on the Moselle, neck around neck in effortless union, slithering smooth between peaks, salt and blood, the taste of glory.

Meanwhile I sulk in a swirl of single malt. Carnita, made and maker. Her exhibition slays me. She becomes her story, milling food into pornography, water into wine, the high priestess of loins marking intimacy as stations of the cross, stigmata cherry on her palms, guiltless deep throat witness reporting on deviant pleasures. She took the lesson seriously, the slice, grind and roll, dew trickling between her shoulders, shining oil on swollen veins, kneading hands cupping flesh to fill limp stockings until a delicate stiffness gives purpose to the exercise, and though raw as fruit, she puts it in her mouth, pushing against her tongue, her own muscles rippling to dominate, stay in control, swallow.

I choke back a gasp, suck scotch from my ice cubes, scribble a few notes on Goethe and food poisoning. Did I really just watch Carnita eat raw meat? Could I mimic her instinct for fantasy? Could I inhale the bestial terroir of alpine pastures and exhale bare skin quivering in the Black Forest? Probably not. Licking juice from her fingers, a froth of mead on her lips, she's a natural, totally absorbed in the act of encasing, enclosing, engorging one animal with another, a milkmaid with grass stains on her back and a whip in her hand. Yet, I aspire to her greatness.

I Could Be Wrong

III
GAMER

35. The Lady Belcher

The Lady Belcher was immaculately coiffed, having spent hours in the mirror twisting the curls around her face into perfect ringlets. She wore a blue silk dress patterned with impressionistic blossoms, as though Monet had painted it himself. Her necklace was strung with jade. A diamond watch encircled her tiny wrist, adorning her sleek hands and painted nails, and her wedding ring dazzled the sun. It was with great irony then that she took the can to her lips, pressed her Peach Sunset lipstick into the aluminum, gulped loudly, filled her cheeks with air, swallowed hard, and let it rip from her belly up her throat into the roof of her mouth, until she could feel the vibration in her nasal passages, a gastric eruption that might have torn a hole in the neck of a lesser woman. But my mother was a champion belcher. Picture Belching Barbie.

One of my least favorite bodily functions is belching. When I hear that throaty sound, I imagine a spout of green gas spewing forth, tumbling sour clouds. My mother thought belching cleansed her digestive tract. If she belched before she went out on social occasions, she was far less likely to fart at the dinner table, or hiccup in the ear of her dance partner. So, once she was all dressed up and ready to go, she made a ritual of producing a big belch with her preferred inducement, 7-Up, a froggy burble rippling up her esophagus and catching in a fleshy rasp. It was one of her lady secrets. She belched the Queen's Belch.

I think she learned this habit from her mother. My grandmother was more of a Lady Burper than a Lady Belcher, but she employed the cleansing act just the same. Lady Burper was also posh in her dainty pink frocks and matching jewelry, white gloves on Sunday, rhinestones around her eyeglasses. Each day at four o'clock, a time when her ancestors might have been enjoying high tea, she sat in her livingroom and had one Salem cigarette, and one Miller High Life beer in a longneck bottle, which she sipped with her lips pursed and her pinkie extended, in noble fashion. Of course, she drank her beer from the bottle because she liked the bubbles, and you know what that means. Just a few minutes after her last swallow a slight shudder would quake her shoulders, her eyes would drift, and a soft thump of air would rise through her chest to gust between her rosy lips. "Oh, dear," she would giggle, each time, as though she were surprised.

Lady Belcher and Lady Burper — these were the women who trained me to be a lady and I loved them. In their company I understood that there were rules a proper woman must follow to be socially accepted, and then I saw that being ladylike was just a game we played.

I Could Be Wrong

X
SALE
MINIMALIST

36. How to Downsize & Start Over

A few years after my husband died, I realized I needed to downsize and start over. But I didn't want to. I wanted to hold onto everything I had because my stuff was my history, my identity, my nest and my friend. Still, as a widow, I couldn't maintain the lifestyle I was accustomed to, couldn't manage the load of expenses, the burdens of homeownership, and the care and feeding of a farm, the house, the outbuildings, the animals and the land. I loved the life I had, but my responsibilities were smothering me, my obligations were eating up all my time, and my brain was overpopulated with statistics like cost of living, interest rates, taxes, debt and resale value. I had to learn how to downsize and start over to find myself again.

I had spent decades decorating my house, curating my look, foraging for coolness and strutting my panache. Then I brought in a couple dealers to see how much money I could get for a lifetime of objects. My ears curled when one woman said most of my stuff was crap. Another said my stuff was out of style. They both said my possessions weren't worth what I thought they were worth, and they suggested I look up my stuff on Ebay to see the real price of things. There I learned the internet is a global tag sale, and my houseful of stuff was competing on price with stuff in Kansas and Georgia. To downsize, I had to give up the idea that my stuff was worth money.

Getting rid of so much of my history made me feel worthless, like I was throwing away my time. Selling my tractor was the first hurdle in giving up my identity as a farmer. I felt my grandmother's hot breath when I sold her china teacups for $1 at a tag sale and had to give away all those embroidered pillowcases. A hundred manly men showed up for the tool sale in my husband's workshop. It was a circus, and when it was over, I missed my husband. So much of my life was encapsulated in my stuff.

I was a member of Hoarder Nation. Stuff is a communicable disease. It comes in contact with our egos, drains our wallets, and multiplies to consume all available space. I lived like the purpose of life is to get stuff, and the purpose of work is to get the money to buy stuff. I endured a lifetime of stress for the status of stuff. When I was unhappy, I could reach out and touch my stuff, and it gave me comfort. My stuff was always there for me, a permanent reminder of who I was and what I had achieved.

I lost a map of myself when I let go of my stuff. But to change my life, I had to change my mind. To change my mind, I needed new surroundings. I had to downsize and start over to discover a fresh perspective. Now I'm redesigning my life. A new me blooms in the richness of my experience. I have more freedom than I've ever had before, and I'm looking forward, enjoying the elegance of a simpler life.

I Could Be Wrong

IV
HUNTER

37. Swipe Left

Eight years after my husband died, every man I saw had a checkbox beside his face. Would I, or wouldn't I? Under the right circumstances, I might. I probably could. I probably would. If he loved me. If he at least seemed like he might love me. I told myself parables of waiting for love, poignant tales of delayed gratification. I dreamed, I flirted, I bought some high heels and flashed some cleavage, I hid the sharp pointy parts of my personality and tried to be feminine and demure, I spoke softly and carried a big stick, desperate to be part of a couple again, to disappear into another person's life, to make their mission my mission, their world my world. I wanted a man to distract me from myself.

As a last resort I went looking for a boyfriend on a matchmaker website and set up a coffee date with a cute guy my age who had a very well written profile. He seemed smart. He was interested in classic cars and bluegrass music and lived a half hour away. Then over cappuccino he told me he had four children from two previous marriages, and he was looking for his soul mate. My brain seized up. I didn't know what to say. I lacked the social skills for a completely phony conversation. All I could think of was, *Give me a break, asshole.* But I didn't say that. I just politely cut him loose.

On the matchmaker website sliding down the page through search results for my ideal guy was like scrolling through a list of vacation destinations. I tried to imagine being there, what I would wear, things I would do, how good I would feel in this fantasy place. I imagined being rescued from my life by another person with a much better life. I could just disappear into him and leave my own world behind. It would be like never having to do laundry again. All my dirty laundry would just take care of itself.

But after my one coffee date, scrolling through lists of men on dating websites was more like looking at used cars. I checked their age first and I was skeptical of anything that looked too perfect. I wanted to see a complete report of the physical condition of the vehicle and the repair history of the engine. I wanted a clean bill of health, a full body scan that showed no weird shaped moles, no fatty liver syndrome, no diabetes, and working plumbing. The worst thing that could happen to me would be to get into a new relationship with a cool guy and have him breakdown and kick the bucket.

When I finally found a guy and contemplated the possibility of a new relationship with someone my own age, I could see the journey was fraught with peril. The clock was ticking and there was no time for years of dating. Couplehood served a practical purpose. It was a safety net. Caregiving was expected. Chronic illness was part of the deal. When we tried to share living space, our boundaries and expectations repelled. Old habits died hard or didn't die at all. Forgetting was tainted by fear of dementia. I learned that sex, intimacy, sleeping together, and actually sleeping, were each discrete functions. Elder cohabitation was a bumpy ride, not the easy flow of youthful synergy. It was a process of negotiation and compromise. Concessions were measured risks. Romance is a drug. Some of us are addicted. Some of us are allergic.

I Could Be Wrong

VI
DOCTOR

38. Hot Flash Fiction

I've been having hot flashes lately. They're waking me up at night with a sudden jolt of wasabi that renders me instantly moist, slick as a frog from scalp to toe. It happens so fast I don't notice it starting, suddenly it's just there on my skin, the largest organ in my body. Damp me. I'm 67. The voice in my head says this menopause is complete. Over. I've moved on with my life, transcended my hormones, escaped the clutches of my lady parts. But, no. There's an untamed creature swimming in me and she likes the humidity. I drag my laptop into bed to see what Dr. Google has to say.

Now I'm wide awake in the blue light. The search results are disappointing. I want to find a 20-year study of 10,000 women between the ages of 40 and 80 that could tell me what's normal, what's to be expected, and what solutions are available to mitigate the symptoms and side effects of menopause. But no such study exists. The rabbit hole of women's medicine beckons, but I give up on science and turn to the arts. My search on "great works of literature about menopause" is equally disappointing. Why can't I find my 67-year-old self in the literary canon of my time?

By now my hot flash has evaporated, in its place existential anxiety and a thin gruel of adrenaline. I want a story where I see myself in the characters and their lives, a story I can relate to even if it took place two hundred years ago, an epic tale of aging women reaching the pinnacle of power as their hormones go wildly wrong, whiskers sprout, they fight sweat stains and embarrassing pee breaks, their egos bruise easily because they've idealized their youth, a subversive fat accumulates around them, and in the heat of battle they realize their superpower is wisdom and resilience, not sex. But my search turns up no such book. The literary canon of menopause has yet to be written.

By the wee hours of the morning I'm a bug-eyed info junkie searching obsessively for one comforting byte of content. Then I stumble on Flash Fiction, a recently evolved literary genre of pithy assemblage that invites the reader to fill in the details with their own imagination. Often a Flash Fiction story will be only a page or two of text. Sometimes Flash Fiction is only six words, a micro-story. For example, this famous six-word epic:

For sale: baby shoes, never worn.

I think, yes! This is what I've been missing, a new literary genre perfect for illuminating the exotic experience of menopause — the body changes that create the behavior changes that change the way we think — and I begin to write Hot Flash Fiction.

Wild mood swing traps unsuspecting man.

Dinner party ruined by sweaty woman.

Couple begins talking after sex fails.

Invisible woman disappears in brain fog.

Brazilian man invents miracle menopause cure.

Rotund woman buys size six wardrobe.

Rotund woman sells size six wardrobe.

Menopause year three, found my keys.

I Could Be Wrong

WILD CARD
HOT FLASH

39. Inhale Exhale

I shaved my winter rabbits this morning. Didn't really want to, love the soft tawny fur, the way it swirls and curls, the whiff of wilting parsley. But rabbit fur and linen just don't go together, and it is officially linen season. I can't help it. I've been imprinted by the old ladies who raised me. They are the ghosts in my closet. When I reach for a little summer dress or a sleeveless top, I hear their voices. Not with the rabbits, dear. My grandmother always called me dear. So, the rabbits had to go, tufts of fur circling toward the shower drain, not to return until sweater season, when I'll grow them again. I'll miss looking at them in the morning when I stretch in the mirror. I'll miss fluffing them with a bath towel. I'll miss sniffing them and wondering who else can smell them.

My grandmother was pristine. She used to brag about what a gentleman my grandfather was, how he wore a bow tie every day and never smelled. That's the difference between my grandmother and me. She powdered her girdle. I raised rabbits. I like the way men smell. I like the smell of people, the aura that floats from their skin through their clothes into their personal space. Pandemic isolation has me missing those traces of our humanness. My nose used to know what my friends smelled like the way it knew my mother and my husband. There is a comfort that comes with inhaling the familiar. I'm longing for the scent of loved ones.

My nose has memories that I forget until they sail through my nostrils into the catalog of my history and record their presence on the list of things I'll always remember. I'm sure you know what I mean. There are smells like music that connect us with a person or a place from way back yonder and we are transported into that experience, swept over by a feeling, dipped in the waters of time. I miss being physically close to people. Never thought I'd be lusting after body odor, but I want proximity. Not the wisps of cologne that linger in the elevator. The real human radiance of moist skin, wet rabbits on a breeze, last night's adventure seeping through pores, a primordial connection with a member of my species I may not have even seen, but we passed through each other's cloud and my nose registered their humanity.

In the country on warm nights we used to say the air was close. Heavy air clung to us. We fanned ourselves on the porch rippling our scent into the dark blue night to mix with the glow of moon flowers and hang in faint mist over the lawn. Now I'm dreaming of those nights, wishing for that closeness, hoping for everyone I know to inhale the gospel of the season and exhale fondness, familiarity, and comfort in lusty human breath, the treasure of our time.

I Could Be Wrong

VIII
QUEEN

40. Pancakes – a modern parable

Good Queen Elder woke on her 80th birthday and she had a big idea. Her eyes sparkled, her hair shimmered silver, and her jewelry shook and danced when she moved. "Today is the day," she said. "Today, I will change the world."

Her Elder Sisters gathered around her and agreed. "Today is the day, Good Queen. Today is the day we change the world."

A throng of Wise Grandmothers gathered in the square and Good Queen Elder spoke to them. "Gather your aprons and your spoons and march with me," she said. "Wake your people. We must have long tables, and everyone must have a seat. Tell your people to come to the table. Then feed them. Feed them pancakes! Everyone must sit and have pancakes!"

Thousands of Wise Grandmothers marched in long parades through every town and village spreading the message of Good Queen Elder. "We must have long tables," they said. "And everyone must have a seat." Along the way people woke up and began to follow the Wise Grandmothers until their parade was so big it filled the streets.

The children picked blueberries and peaches and apples and bananas for the pancakes. Some collected syrup from the trees and some put flowers on the long tables. Farmers brought their eggs and milk and grain. Everyone helped. Then the Wise Grandmothers raised their spoons and began to stir. And they stirred and stirred and stirred and stirred. Until pancakes began to fly to the table.

A pancake on every plate! It was a feast! As they ate the pancakes the people became pleasant. Anger became kindness. Sadness became sweet. When everyone shared the table, no one was afraid. The Wise Grandmothers made pancakes until all the hungry people were served. Then Good Queen Elder stood and smiled.

"Remember this moment," she said. "When we share a table, we share ourselves. To change the world, we must share. To give is simple, to share is wise."

The Wise Grandmothers raised their spoons to honor Good Queen Elder, and the people looked across the table at each other and felt kindness, and their kindness brought peace, and peace changed the world.

Was it magic? No.

Was it war? No.

Was it technology? No.

It was pancakes.

I Could Be Wrong

IIII
EXPLORER

41. Date with a Spider

I once went on a date with a spider. I was supposed to be on a date with a man, but the spider was the only thing I could think about. For days. What is a date, really? A brief excursion into future possibilities for life together, a toe dipped in the waters of emotional investment, a test drive of body parts and attention spans, a feast for the communion of souls or a quick trip to Taco Bell. My starting place is a feast for the communion of souls, exfoliating, the little black dress, lipstick that doesn't smear. If I find myself overdressed at Taco Bell, I've learned something. Dating serves as much to teach me about myself as it does to teach me about my date. That spider taught me something.

The guy was my age, a retired Wall Street math wiz, big house, animal lover, wine collector, never married. In the corner of my mind where my stupidity resides, I think a rich man who has never been married must be the fairytale prince who has waited his whole life just for me. What should inspire skepticism sparks a fantasy of perfect timing. Destiny. This thought occurs even though I have been warned about this guy by women at parties, the same parties where I've seen him on a few occasions with a few different women. But I project failure onto those women and see myself as a superior match for the man who must have everything. This, of course, is delusional.

We had planned to go on a picnic in his car, so we met in his driveway. In general, I would say men should not wear plaid Bermuda shorts on a first date, but I was willing to make exceptions. When I asked to use his bathroom, he pointed to the back door of the house. "It's through the kitchen on the left," he said. "You'll have to share it with Donna." I opened the door to a large kitchen with an island and a diningroom and livingroom beyond. Windows all around filled the space with natural light and just as I was about to inventory his possessions there was a skittering movement in my peripheral vision that made me jump. It was a spider on a web that was at eye level, a web that stretched from a stack of frying pans on the stovetop up to the greasy hood extending over the burners, a web the size of a soccer ball dotted with flecks of dead flies, and attended by a furry brown spider of the sort I had seen crawling in my basement. I know something about spiders. They like to pitch their webs in the airflows that carry flying insects. Spiders and mice are a fact of life in the country.

In the bathroom I learned that Donna was a house cat who enjoyed her own private powder room with the litter box in the center of the rug and cat litter scattered to the four corners. The cat box was not clean. But I have had house cats. I put the dirty cat box in the guest bathroom in the same category as the plaid Bermuda shorts. It was a mistake that could be corrected. But a huge brown spider defending a well-established web, strung in the cooking area of the kitchen from the Calphalon to the microwave, obvious and menacing, in a place that, to my way of thinking, would be the busiest place in the kitchen, on the stove, beside the back door, at eye level. That was a sign from the Goddess of Lost Socks. There's something missing here. What kind of guy has a spider web like that in his kitchen? I decided right then that I was never going to know.

I Could Be Wrong

XII
ICONOCLAST

42. Black Hole

I have a black hole on the left side of my face near my nose. It's been there almost my whole life. Years ago, when I went to a dermatologist to remove a small cyst from my earlobe, he looked at my black hole and gasped as though he'd never seen anything so wild and strange on a person's face. He actually said, I've never seen anything like that! And in my mind, I heard the sound of a cash register going cha-ching! He then told me what a shame it was to have something so dark and ugly spoil my look. With faux kindness he took pity on what must be my shattered ego. He assured me he could remove the unsightly blemish and restore my self-esteem. Yeah. Not so much. Self-esteem has never been my problem. He said he saw his mission in life as correcting people's flaws so they could discover their true selves and be happy. Honestly, he was just a Good Samaritan with a scalpel. Cha-ching!

The thing is, my black hole is my true self. When I told him, I was keeping it as a souvenir of my childhood his eyes crossed, and I thought he might pass out. Maybe he was missing a boat payment. But he didn't ask me why. He didn't make the effort to understand what had happened to me that might make that mark on my face important. He wasn't trying to be my friend or my therapist. We weren't having a conversation. This was a sales pitch. He was selling me by shaming me and then telling me how he could relieve my shame. He was my savior. Cha-ching!

If he hadn't been such a jerk, I might have taken him seriously. My black hole is an inconvenience. In my early days of wearing makeup base and now in my sunscreen days, it fills with goo and that looks icky. If he had said, doesn't your makeup get stuck in there? I might have listened to him. But the idea of being shamed into cosmetic surgery just pissed me off. It was one thing to have the cyst in my earlobe removed. I could feel it when I put on my pierced earrings and it was making them hang crooked. I'm cool with a scar on my face. But we can't have crooked earrings.

My black hole is a chicken pox scar from the early days of my childhood when my mother was expected to manage three children through what we then called the childhood diseases: measles, mumps and chicken pox, all highly contagious airborne infections that in the 1960s kids were expected to get and survive. In those days the only vaccine we got was for polio, environmental pollution had yet to weaken our immune systems, all the food we ate was homemade, we played outside all day, we got dirty, and we were resilient. I was covered with chicken pox blisters, they itched like crazy and I picked at them until they bled. My mother trimmed my nails and warned me not to scratch. She told me picking scabs would create scars. But I was a kid. The scars on my knees were a badge of honor. They were stories of how I hurt myself and survived, stories of falling down, getting up and moving on. Those are stories I still need to remember.

I Could Be Wrong

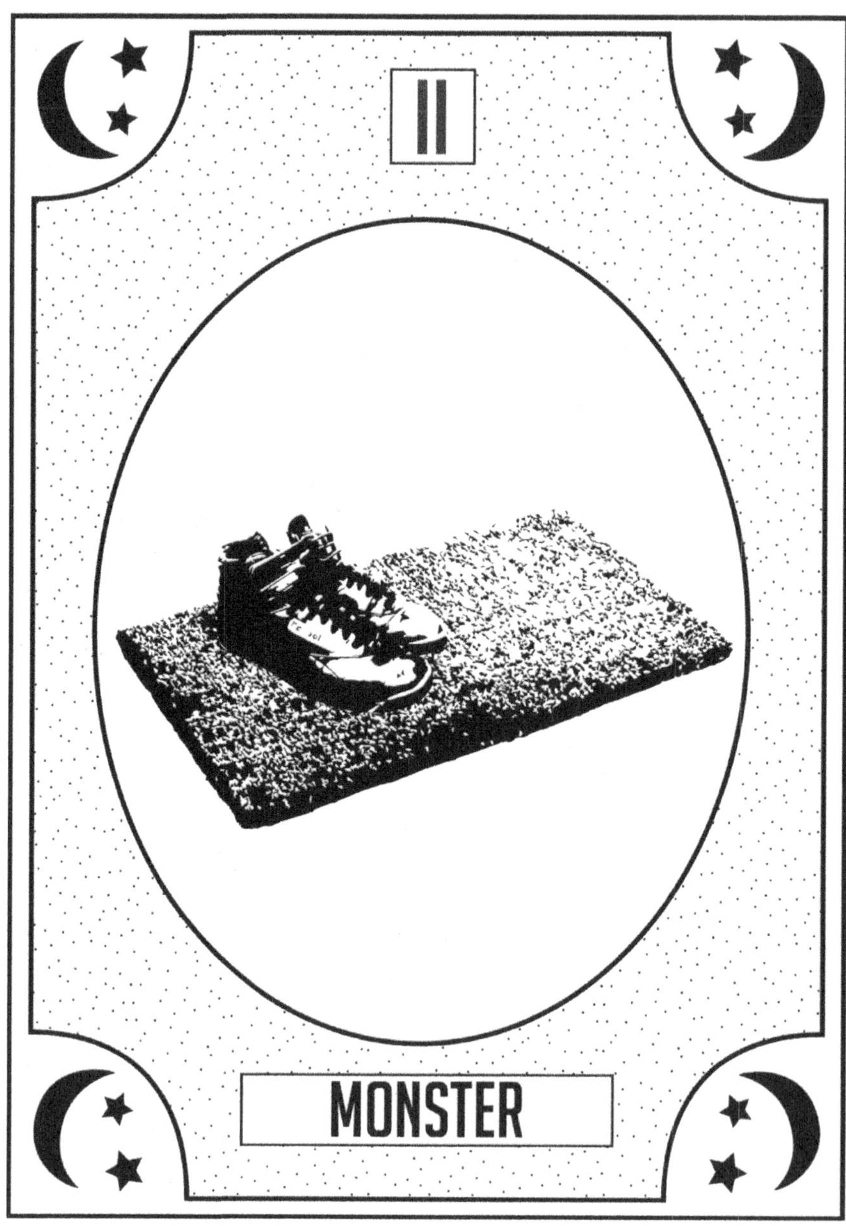
II
MONSTER

43. Fear of Forgetting

I was feeding my dog, Moon, breakfast, filling his water and food bowls, while I was thinking about my shoes, trying to decide if I need a new pair of super bouncy sidewalk shoes. The season is changing, and so are the rules for color. I just don't know if I can wear my cute pink Skechers in November. My mother drilled it into me that white and pastels are the palette from Memorial Day to Labor Day, after which we wear earth tones, until holiday when we switch to jewel tones. Even though that sounds like a lot of old school BS — which it is — after all these years, that's how my eyes see color. So, I definitely can't wear pink walkers in winter, I say to myself, as I'm pouring water over Moon's kibble and placing his food bowl on his doggy placemat in the kitchen.

On the other hand, white shoes are really in style right now. Can I wear my white leather Reeboks in winter? It doesn't feel right. Reeboks take me back to the 1980s when I lived in Boston, and women's athletic shoes became a symbol of our new fitness focus. Reeboks were the first shoe brand to spotlight women athletes. Back then I wore sweatpants and did jumping jacks. Cybill Shepherd wore a pair of orange Reeboks to the Emmys in 1985. She said she was so sexy she didn't have to wear high heels. All this nostalgia was billowing through my mind as I rinsed Moon's water bowl and refilled it.

These days athletic shoes are called trainers, sneakers, tennis shoes, or running shoes. Everybody wears them, even if they're not training, sneaking, playing tennis, or running, and the color patterns are garish, the uglier the better. All the big fashion brands are doing ugly shoes. By noon I'm still mentally in shoe world, scrolling through websites, reminiscing about my first pair of clogs, remembering platforms and wedgies, browsing wedgie sneakers. Then Moon wants lunch, and his water bowl is missing. The place where it should be on his doggie placemat is empty. I have the insane thought, How did he do that? How does a dog move his water bowl without spilling it? I know I filled it. I know it. Then I get all spooky with myself about dementia because I can't find my dog's full water bowl, or any spilled water.

Meanwhile Moon is pacing. I focus on feeding him as I plan for my imminent demise. I'm must have Alzheimer's. My mom did. If I can't find my dog's water bowl, how do I even know where I am? Dying of dementia is going to be really sad. I better go shoe shopping now while I can still remember how to get home. Tearfully, I put my coat on and then I see it. There on the front doormat beside my Reeboks is Moon's full water bowl. Yup. I'm definitely losing my mind.

I Could Be Wrong

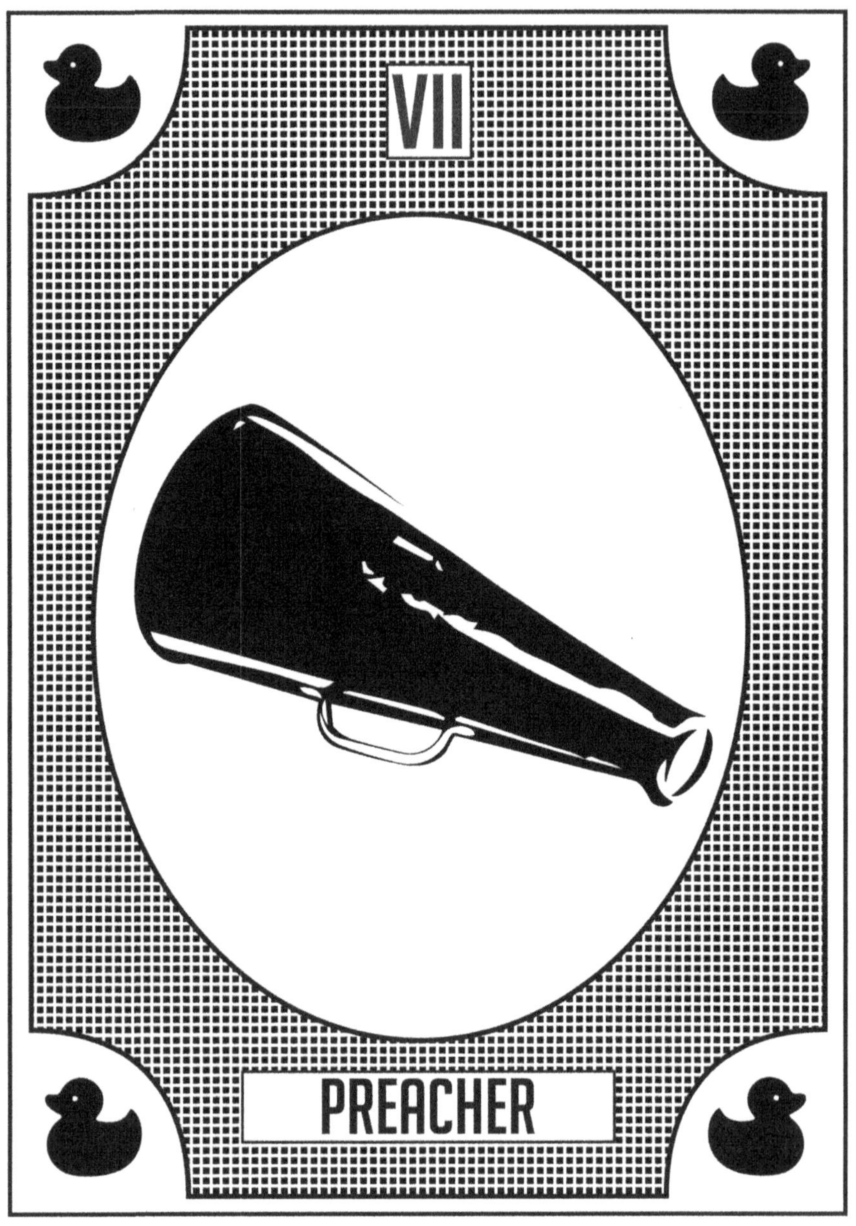
VII
PREACHER

44. Our Collective Diapers

In high school they called me the Class Arguer. I was an angry teenager and I was up for an aggressive disagreement on any topic — how I dressed, how I spoke, how I spent my time, how I danced, how I wore my hair. You name it, I could stake out an opinion and defend it. I come from a very verbal gene pool. I learned to read and write early. I'm a talker. I've always been this way. Give me a topic and I'll give you a diatribe. Debate is my superpower.

So, as you might imagine, I could have a lot to say right now about all the happenings in the world. I've got a mouthful of opinions waiting behind the gates of social acceptance to spew forth in unmitigated self-importance and the blind ecstasy of righteousness. Please, nail me to the cross of my sentence structure and hold me accountable for my sassiness, because I've got some paragraphs in here just waiting to rip through your confirmation bias and sink your ship of state. Boy, oh, boy, am I angry. But who cares? Really. Who cares what I think?

No one. Precisely no one cares what I think. Most likely because their brains are already fully occupied by what they think. And that's fine. We should all be thinking right now. We have painted ourselves into a corner here with all our rules that don't solve our problems and all our problems that don't fit with our preconceived ideas about how things should work. Our entire civilization is stuck in adult diapers throwing a temper tantrum over the painful rash. But we used up all our clean water on legal pollution. Our personal protective equipment is stuck in a trade war between tribes who think they're special even though we all share the same biology.

The new buzz word is "lizard brain" — a phrase that implies our intelligence is shrinking from analysis to knee jerk. Our rash has made us irrational.

Oh, yes, I'm angry. But here's the thing about my anger: Anger is not a solution. My need to express it is much greater than your need to hear it. My need to say what I think is much greater than your need to know. My need to vent is much greater than your capacity to absorb it. That's what's out of balance in the world. Our oversupply of anger is tipping us into catastrophe. Meanwhile our rash burns.

How did we all get so angry? Do we spend too much time listening to anger? Are you a doom scroller? Maybe it's just anger that's making us so angry. There's a lot of money to be made in anger. Is your anger somebody's income? Keeping us angry is a way to manipulate us. Look who's pimping anger. Our anger is creating chaos. It's burning up our resources. Time to focus, organize, get a grip on the excrement of our fear, cleanse the anger from our minds, and redesign the future of our species. Stop the burn. Our collective diapers need changing.

I Could Be Wrong

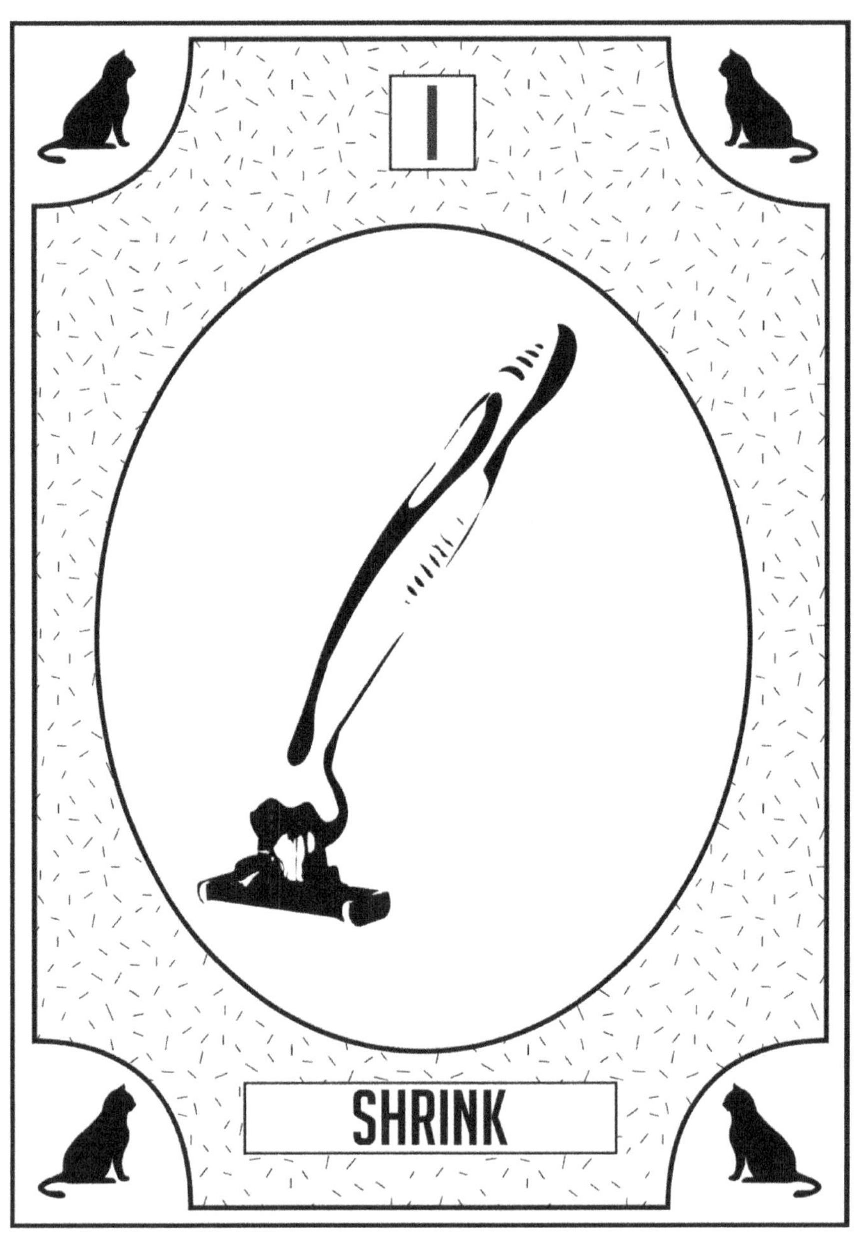
I
SHRINK

45. I Shaved My Legs

I shaved my legs this morning. It was a leap of faith. I truly believe I'm going out again someday. So, I put on a dress and some lipstick just for practice. I don't want to lose my social skills just because I'm in solitary confinement with my dog and some raggedy houseplants. I'm looking forward, imagining a July 4th barbeque with friends crowded around a table of homemade food, swilling pitchers of iced tea and eating fearlessly with our fingers. It might be 2021, but it's definitely going to happen.

After I put my glasses on, I had to shave my legs again. Missed a few places. I wish I liked the hair on my legs, but I don't. All winter long the mangy wires are hidden under long pants and socks. But spring is here and it's warm enough to go outside flesh exposed. Of course, no one is looking at my legs but me, and you might say, who cares? And ordinarily I would be a little defensive and admit my ego is out of control. However, these days my ego is the dotted line between me and my sanity. I'm looking for things to care about in a world where the list of what really matters is getting shorter and shorter. My ego keeps me on the list. How I feel matters. Isolation is a slippery slope into self-deprecation, depression and dementia. I have an advanced degree in all three, and, well, frankly, I can't afford the weight gain. The first thing that happens to me when I get depressed is I drink, which leads me to eating, which leads me to pizza and ice cream, which leads me to a midnight rendezvous with the leftover pizza and ice cream, or drinking maple syrup out of the bottle.

I was once so depressed that I ate an entire cheesecake by myself. I am 5′2″ and I ballooned to a size 14 pants with a D-cup bra. My cheeks were made of mashed potatoes and my arms were Christmas hams. I can't do that to myself again. It took too long to learn to eat right and lose my craving for gravy, because the problem with gravy is it tastes best with a pot roast, and when I eat that much meat in one sitting, I don't shit for days. I went for a gynecological exam and the doctor was alarmed by the bricks of sediment in my abdomen. She sent me home with an enema kit and a little box of laxatives and warned me about the dangers of colon cancer. So, you see, that's why I shaved my legs today — to keep from getting colon cancer.

There are many ways to approach self-preservation, and each of us must choose our own path. For me, shaving my legs, wearing a dress, and putting on lipstick straightens my spine, squares my shoulders, and gives me the strength to lean into a day that is just like yesterday, and all the days last week. A blind leap of faith is what it is. There's still the possibility that something fabulous is going to happen. I wake up every day believing that, and it gets me through the acres of time between when I place my order and when my pizza delivery finally arrives. Yes, I've completely rationalized it. I'm taking a day off from judging myself. This melted cheese is for my soul.

I Could Be Wrong

XI
JUDGE

46. My Menopause Conspiracy Theory

I'm developing a conspiracy theory about menopause. It doesn't include UFOs or assassinations or Elvis. My menopause conspiracy theory is that a couple hundred years ago, as women were becoming more educated and the Industrial Revolution was replacing men with machines, Mary Shelley put the cherry on top of men's fear of being replaced when she wrote her famous book about sewing a big guy together from spare body parts and making him beg for a girlfriend. As her intelligence shocked the world men moved aggressively to stop women from taking power and becoming equal.

Frankenstein was published in 1818 by the daughter of the feminist philosopher Mary Wollstonecraft who died in 1797, eleven days after birthing the author. Yes, the first and most famous literary work of science fiction was written by a teenage girl, Mary Wollstonecraft Shelley. She wasn't allowed to be educated at university, so she took it upon herself to study anatomy and electricity and imagine how they might be combined to create a man who wanted only to please.

In that era there was a broad social movement of men determined to stop women from becoming experts in any field. Pregnancy had been the way to control women's lives. But once a woman lived past her childbearing years and had her own agency, she could compete with men for jobs, property and leadership. Hence the popular myth that menopause damages women beyond repair. Instead of allowing us to compete, they shunned us. If you think I'm exaggerating just google Freud and menopause.

Enter big pharma and menopause has become the Area 51 of medicine with alien forces sapping a woman's hormones, rendering her unattractive, mentally weak, sexless and hysterical. Or imagine menopause as Mother Nature kissing off a woman's reproductive obligations, launching her into a personal renaissance of wisdom, empowerment and independence. As with all conspiracy theories, you get to choose what to believe.

For example, tell me if this sounds familiar. A woman is very uncomfortable for many months, her body does strange things without warning, she is misshapen and loses her mind on occasion, followed by enormous doubts that she can really make it through the ordeal. And then finally she does, and she is a hero in her own mind because she knows the feelings she has managed and understands the extremes of physical and emotional change she can endure. When it's over, she's a different person living a different life in a different body, renewed by her own spirit, transformed by her experience, and enlightened by her connection to the life force. So — is this menstruation, pregnancy or menopause?

The conspiracy of men to hold women back from power by disparaging our minds and bodies is evident in the facts of history and today in the disproportionately small number of midlife women in leadership. The first step in overcoming the deep social prejudice engendered by this conspiracy is to celebrate the changes in our bodies as we age and appreciate how those changes build our strength.

I Could Be Wrong

XIII
THINKER

47. I Could Be Wrong

I'm giving up my need to be right. It's not that hard for me. My mouth is often unfiltered by my brain, my tongue wags free range and errors drop into my lap like bird poop. Sometimes I know I've said something ridiculous. Other times I cruise right through my misbegotten words onto the next topic and it could be days or even weeks before I realize what I actually said and how dumb it was. The thing is, right now I really don't care that much about being right. I care more about the exploration of my abilities, twirling my thoughts in the air like a cheerleader's baton, tossing them up and catching them again to test my mental acuity, the speed and coordination of my mind, the fun of being funny. I want to be entertaining and I realize sometimes the most entertaining thing about me is my mistakes. If my mistakes make you feel good, that makes me feel good.

My memoir is about 20 years of mistakes I made between my 40s and my 60s. In midlife I hit the peak of my powers as a woman, but having power isn't the same thing as knowing what you're doing. I was feeling the glory of following my passion, high on my dreams, fabulously myopic, and then I crashed and burned. The good news is that recovering from my mistakes made me strong and built my resilience. But I'm not taking anything for granted. My next really big mistake is just around the corner. Knowing it's out there is humbling. So, I'm giving up my need to be right.

I could be wrong about everything. It's a liberating idea. Righteousness is very popular these days. It feels like rebellion to freely admit my ambivalence. But I have a long history of incorrectness in my personal, professional and political life. For instance, as a young ladder climber I thought the government should operate like a for-profit business. This was also the time when I could drink three martinis before wine with dinner and not fall into a coma. I was on my way up in my career, making money for the first time in my life, and I believed in economic Darwinism, survival of the richest. Yes, I was deep breathing my own exhaust, telling myself that the people with more money were better at running the planet.

I've given up my need to be right because my track record stinks. I didn't see how bank deregulation could mushroom into a debt bomb, or how privatization of the public good could lead to utterly inadequate healthcare, or how trickle-down economics would never happen because rich people hoard money. I'm sure someone predicted these calamities, but I didn't see them coming. Now, I can't get it out of my head that in hard times like these where the majority of households lack the cash to solve a $400 problem, and 30 million people are unemployed because the pandemic killed their jobs, limiting unemployment benefits to only 70 percent of their previous relatively low income could be a recipe for increased poverty, social unrest and further economic decline. But, of course, I could be wrong.

I Could Be Wrong

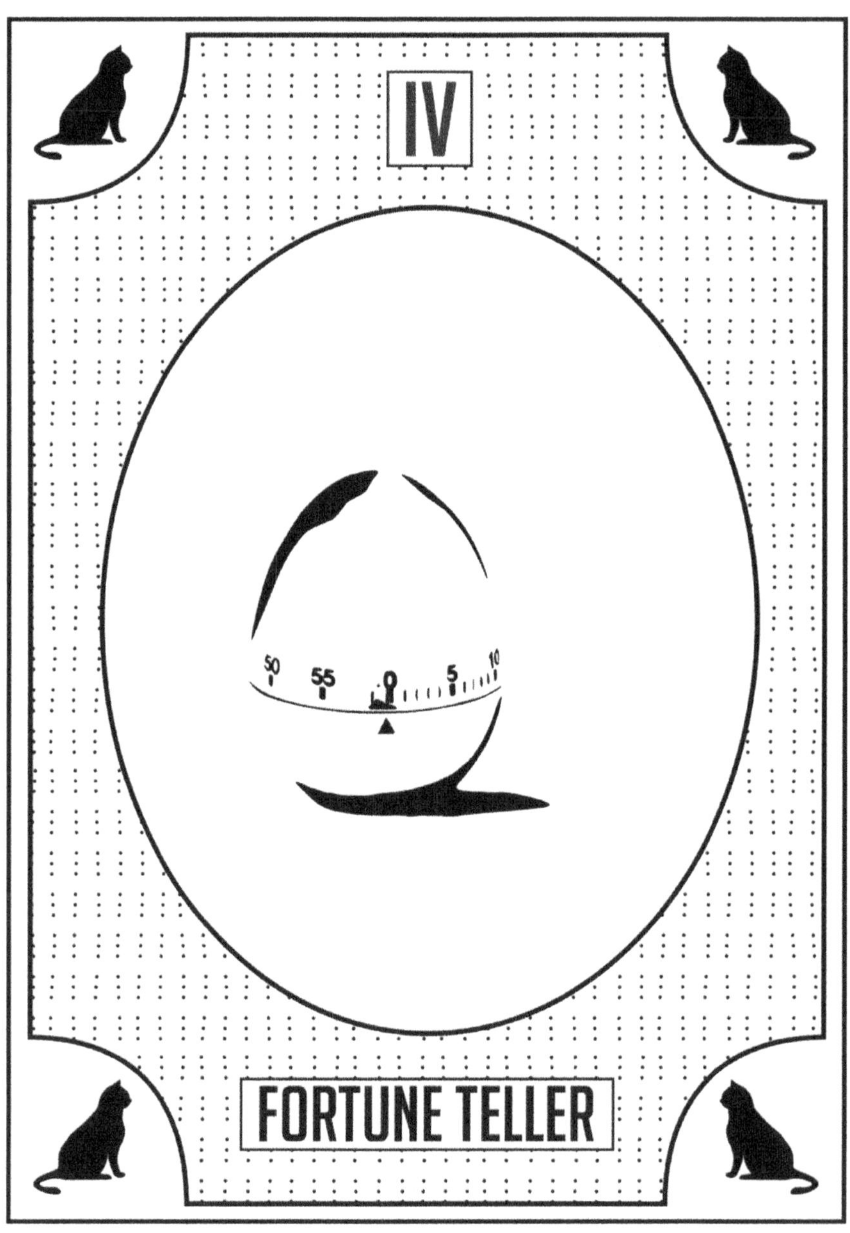
IV
50
55
0
5
10
FORTUNE TELLER

48. Speed Dating

I had a peculiar dream about speed dating in a nursing home. Probably because I've been thinking about the alacrity of elder hook-ups. It's not like when we were young and our parents advised, "Don't rush into anything. Take your time. You've got the rest of your life ahead of you." Fifty years later, when the rest of your life feels near at hand, unconditional love becomes conditional, and speed dating just makes sense. In my dream there were a few old men seated alone at different tables in a big dining room with a long line of old women waiting to sit with them for a three minute chat before an egg timer would ding and the women would move on to the next man at the next table.

When my turn came, I introduced myself and the guy said, "Hello, Betty. That was my first wife's name." And I said, "No, my name is Billie." And he said, "Yes, I know. That was my first wife's name." And I said, "Do you have trouble hearing?" And he said, "No, she died." And I said, "Oh, I'm sorry." And he said, "I don't think I could have another wife named Betty. It would just be too confusing."

Then the egg timer dinged, and I moved on to a table with a white-haired man in a beret holding an unlit pipe between his teeth. Oh, an intellectual, I thought. How nice. And I began to fantasize about vacations in Paris. Then he took the pipe out of his mouth and said, "Can you cook?" And I said, "Yes, I'm a very good cook." "What can you cook?" he asked. There must have been a lot of traffic on the Champs Elysees because I was suddenly overwhelmed by a blinking yellow light and horns honking all around me. He folded his arms across his chest. "I don't like eggs," he said. "What do you cook?" The light turned red. "Hotdogs," I said. "The only thing I cook is hotdogs."

In my dream I had amused myself with that wry answer, but I was also anxious about being alone for the rest of my life, so I took my seat at the next table in front of a guy with a crewcut who scanned my body. "You're not wearing a watch," he said. "How can you be on time if you don't wear a watch?" Instead of answering him, I smirked and waved my phone in the air until he smacked his hand on the table to get my attention. I jumped. "I hate it when women are late," he said. He was the spitting image of my high school math teacher. "Phones tell time now," I said. He squinted in disbelief, the class bell rang, and he started licking my face. I pushed him away and my dog jumped back on the bed and licked my face again until I got up. What a dream. For the rest of the day I psychoanalyzed myself, decoding the messages from my subconscious: You be you. Don't expect a relationship to be a vacation. And don't wait for someone else to love you. Love yourself the way your dog loves you, unconditionally.

I Could Be Wrong

IX
OBSERVER

49. Call Me Penguin

"Call me Ishmael. Some years ago — never mind how long precisely — having little or no money in my purse, and nothing particular to interest me on shore, I thought I would sail about a little and see the watery part of the world. It is a way I have of driving off the spleen and regulating the circulation. Whenever I find myself growing grim about the mouth; whenever it is a damp, drizzly November in my soul; whenever I find myself involuntarily pausing before coffin warehouses, and bringing up the rear of every funeral I meet; and especially whenever my hypos get such an upper hand of me, that it requires a strong moral principle to prevent me from deliberately stepping into the street, and methodically knocking people's hats off—then, I account it high time to get to sea as soon as I can. This is my substitute for pistol and ball."

That's the first paragraph of Moby Dick written in 1851, an ode to the disgruntled man. Looking to escape the drizzly November in his soul, Ishmael ends up on one nasty boat ride. It's a cautionary tale for those of us trying to get a grip on our own hypos, perhaps also fantasizing about knocking people's hats off and substituting nasty comments on social media for pistol and ball. To calm my angst, I've been watching penguin videos on Youtube.

My new influencer could be a chubby seabird with greasy feathers that can't fly. Yes, I'm lowering my expectations. Since I first saw the video of penguins strolling through an art gallery, I've been admiring their incredible lightness of being and wishing I could find myself as curious and inquisitive, filled with wonder, without judgment or dissatisfaction, taking it all in, absorbing the newness without resistance and waddling on. Call me Penguin.

Waddle On could be my new motto. Like many people, I'm looking for a different way of being as I'm cut loose from the moorings of my social life, lunches and happy hours, movies and potluck dinners, jabbering with friends long into the night. My routine is disrupted, lumpy and rattled. For example, my car died because I'm only driving a few miles a week at slow speeds, which is not enough to keep my battery charged. Who knew? Now I see it's my presumption of smoothness that's the problem. I'm nostalgic for a normal that was never static, always shifting, imaginary. Penguins are not preoccupied by the mirage of normal. They are not nostalgic. They don't seem disappointed to be indoors. My first step toward contentment might be to stop judging the present against the past.

In another penguin video the seabird gazes through an aquarium window eye to eye with a white beluga whale. Both captives in a world they did not choose, a world less beautiful than the one they were made for, their eyes meet. But instead of looking through the glass darkly to the imperfections of their reality, you can see their minds open to the newness of each other. They exchange a startled innocence and life goes on. I'm working toward that level of acceptance.

I Could Be Wrong

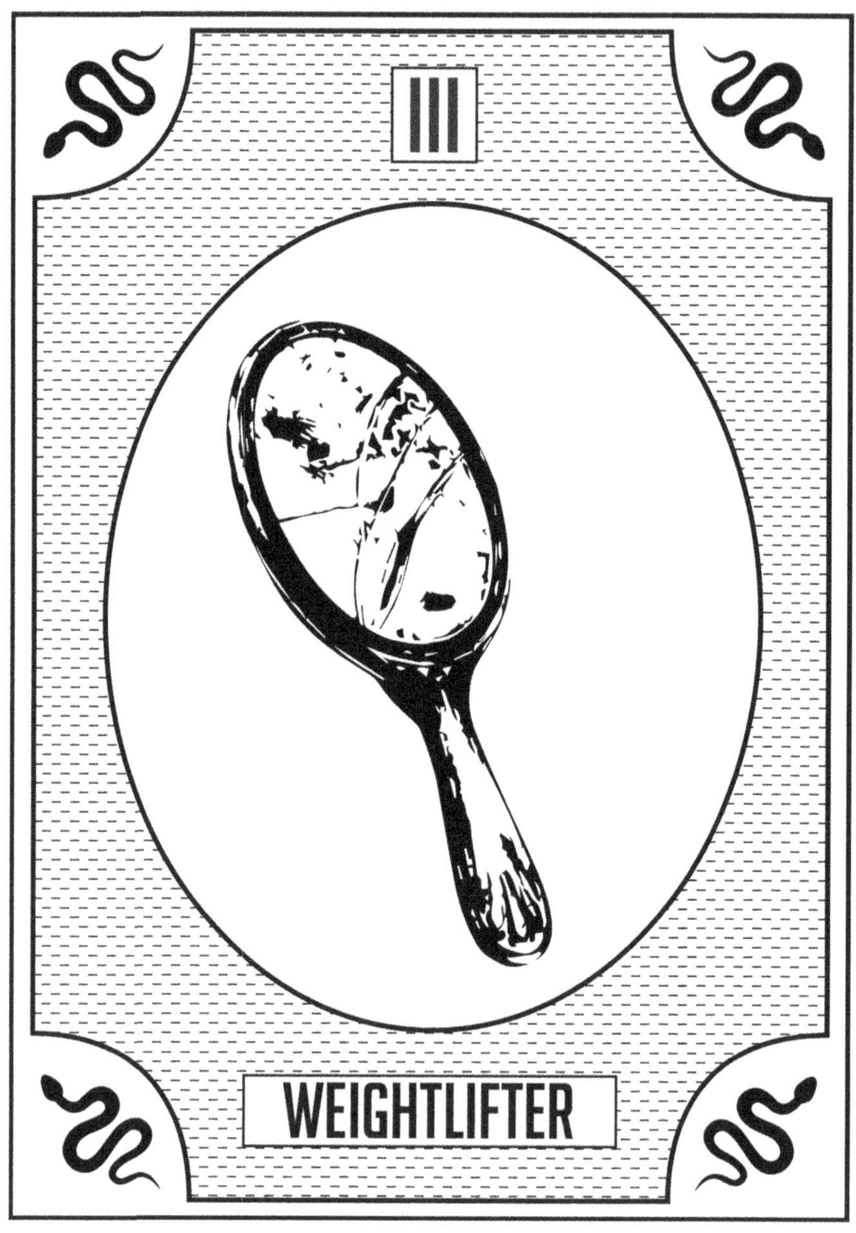
IIII
WEIGHTLIFTER

50. The Cure for Ageism

When I was in my 40's I was afraid of getting old. I fretted over my new wrinkles, started sleeping on my back to prevent my pillow from crushing lines into my cheeks. I pulled out the new grey wires sprouting amongst my brown locks, and for a while, I dyed my hair so no one would notice my frightful change. I worried about menopause, would it ever end, would I suffer permanent brain damage, would I ever lose the weight, would I ever sleep again, would I ever find my keys. I stopped wearing silk blouses because the sweat stains were too depressing. For all the security of my professional accomplishments and the sage wisdom of my experience, which seemed like a lot at the time after 40+ years, I was not wise about aging. I was looking for the cure. That's ageism.

It never occurred to me that there was anything good about getting old. I saw the benefits of old trees to the forest, but I never considered the contributions of old people to the community. I was prejudiced against the physical signs of age, the sags and bags and creases and folds. I associated age with being slow, forgetful and out of touch. The old people around me were my parents and grandparents, their friends and relatives, and I loved them, but I did not see them as my destiny. I did not think of aging as my obligation, a service to my species, a gift to the future. I did not think, oh, how cool it's going to be when I'm 90. I feared aging like lions, and tigers, and bears, oh, my!

It took years to get over the shock of looking in the mirror and seeing my mother. You might think a 66-year-old woman would identify with her own age, but the truth is I still look at other old people and see them as old. That negative characterization is ageism. In my own mind I'm the same person I was 50 years ago cruising bare skinned in short shorts and a pair of boots that could kick holes in the soul of an unsuspecting man. The psychic twist of aging is no matter how old I am, I'm not the one who's getting old. My inner voice remains the same, creating the illusion of youth in my head.

Now the signs of aging that I feared in my 40s — wrinkles, grey hair and menopause — are so incorporated into my being that I don't see them anymore. Likewise, the life changing events of my 50s — broken marriage, death of my husband, downsizing and starting over — are behind me. Been there, done that. These days I'm enjoying the freedom of my new life, the strength built lifting heavy spirits and the resilience gained by bouncing back. Life is a fun ride once more and I don't want to miss anything, so I'm crafting my buzz, soaking up the moment, also probably forgetting something, but whatever. If I seem out of touch it's because everything that matters to me is right here, right now. I'm not searching, not climbing, not waiting. I've arrived. My fear of aging is gone. I just wish my 40-year-old self could have caught a glimpse of me now and been reassured that beauty evolves. Serenity gathers in us and finally we are whole, leaning into the future, fearless of the years.

I Could Be Wrong

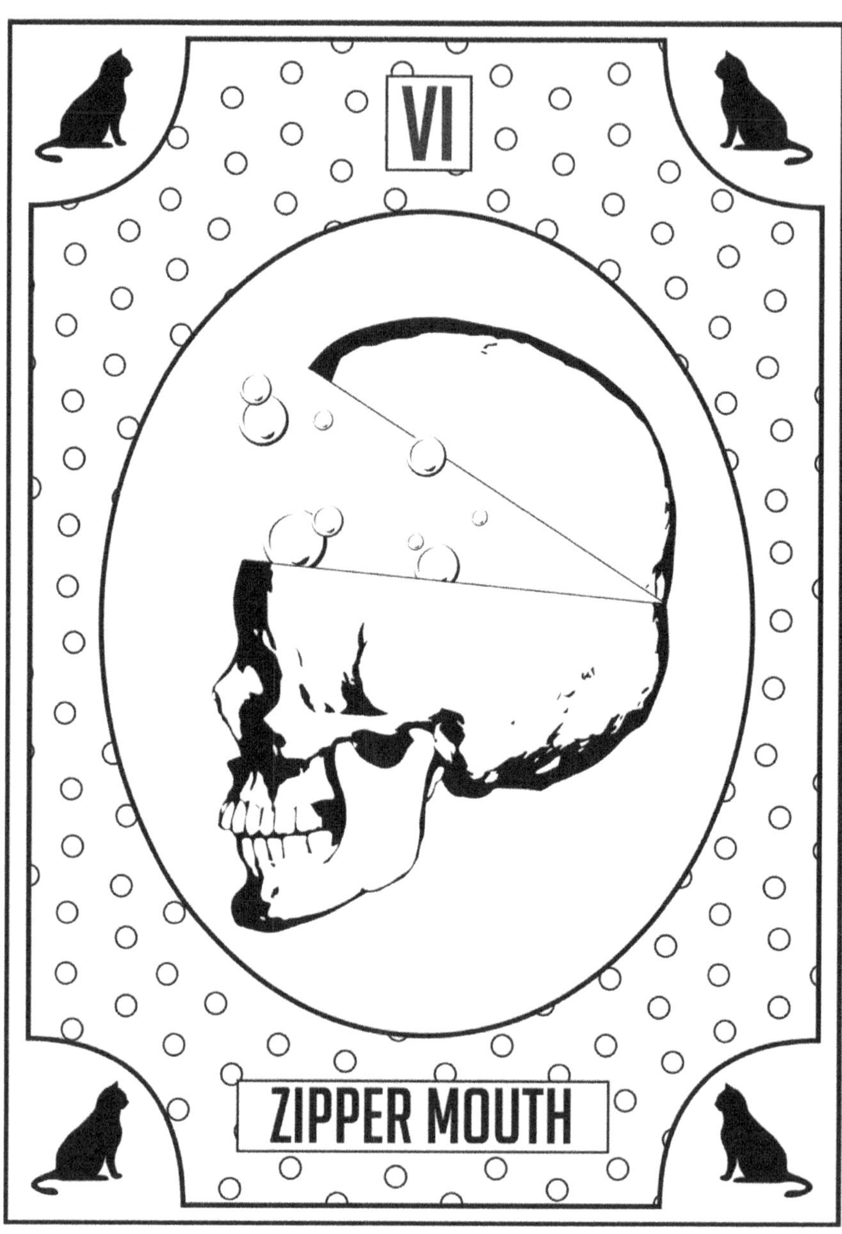
VI
ZIPPER MOUTH

51. Perfecting My Ignorance

I'm arrogant, always thinking I know the answer and quick to let it roll off my lips or my fingers without taking a moment to reconsider. That knowing is a habit. Even when I don't know, I know I know because my knowing is rhetorical, a figure of speech. I know before I think. It's automatic. That's how deeply ingrained in me it is to know. Maybe it's genetic. My father and mother were both authorities on everything. If you were going to speak at our family dinner table, you had better be prepared to properly articulate your case or you would be trapped in a word smackdown with a vocabulary lesson from my mom or a semantics diatribe from my dad. That early training built my skills as an Olympic bullshit artist, with the tiniest tidbit of information I can spin an authoritative story about anything, lots of fun at parties, but probably not right for the International Space Station.

These days I have hit my information horizon. With the ever-expanding scale and scope of world events, my perspective is changing. I'm frightened by the idea that so many people think they have all the answers, know what to believe, buy into a narrative without question. I don't want to be one of those people. There is so much I don't know about what's going on, and yet, I don't want to know anything more. My head is overheating with the pace of change and I need two minutes to idle my thoughts and witness myself, witness how much I don't know about everything. I'm perfecting my ignorance. I've been shunning it when I should have been appreciating it.

Truly intelligent people are inclined to admit what they don't know, and truly stupid people are inclined to think they have all the answers. To avoid confusion between me and a truly stupid person, I'm swearing off answers and admitting my ignorance. Answers let me down. They are a species of idea I'm isolating right now because I don't trust them. Admitting my ignorance relieves my stress. It's like learning a new yoga pose and then trying to hold it for the rest of your life. Awkward but beneficial. It's going to take some practice and it's uncomfortable. It doesn't come naturally to me. My arrogance is hereditary. I'm fighting Nature here. But I've got to do it, set a good example, adjust my own mask before I try to help others, be the change I seek. Here goes...

I don't know. I really don't know. I'm blanking on that. I don't have the answer. I have no idea. I forget. I need more information. I don't have an opinion on that. Not in my wheelhouse. Coming up empty on that one. Never knew. Didn't do my homework. I have no expertise in that area. I never understood that. The answer isn't coming to me right now. Nope, don't know.

I broke out in hives writing that, but I've got to break the habit of thinking I have the answers. That's why I'm perfecting my ignorance.

I Could Be Wrong

IV
MONEY BAGS

52. The Nipple Club (Carnita #3)

Carnita had all the right instincts for how to handle the pandemic. When the book tour for her porn travelogue was cancelled, she instinctively turned her talents to the virtual world and began to engage the audience for her erotic novels through video chat. Her genius exhausts me. I mope with an international cadre of authors whose plans have been cancelled by the virus. When bookstores closed, we sulked while Carnita gathered her fans, a moist communion of velveteen souls, on Zoom. The unique features of that platform were an invitation to exhibitionists. At her Zoom meetings, fans presented themselves naked in her honor, liberated by the safety and privacy of their unknown location, and the Nipple Club was born.

What I saw as an act of desperation, stripping to get attention on Zoom, Carnita saw as her new side hustle. That's the difference between her and me. I skipped bathing and wallowed in my empty calendar, a stubborn victim complaining of lost opportunities. Through the same torpor, Carnita ascended, lit, undaunted by isolation, pimping her vision on social media, fingers deep in the begging black hole of cyberspace teasing out a new kind of satisfaction — crowd-sourced porn. A naked rave. Safe, silent and separate, with the option for anonymity. A way to relieve human solitude without risk of exposure. She was Imagineering virtual intimacy, a harmonic convergence of lust and loneliness, open to the public. Porn church. Come one, come all.

I found this burst of empathy previously missing from her repertoire of genital provocateurs, seducers and soft targets.

Making the connection between intimacy and wellbeing conferred legitimacy on her catalogue. Her book sales spiked. She was crowned queen of erotica. After her first interview on morning TV, I stayed in bed for three days and ate chocolate. Without any formal credentials, she became the darling of schlock producers and magazine sidebars on how to stay mentally healthy in isolation. Jerk off! Really, I thought, that's the cure? Carnita smiled for the cameras and said she wanted the people who felt unseen to be seen. The Nipple Club was therapy. A celebration of the cosmic connection between mother and child since forever.

And so, she built her platform one nipple at a time. No faces, no bodies, no clothes, no possessions, no status stuff. Just nipples or the place where a nipple once was. With a simple set of rules, she made the Nipple Club a safe genderless congregation, absent the messy complication of proximity, all microphones off, each participant in their own solitary box, exposing their unit, sharing, wholesome as a mother's love. When the History Channel interviewed her for a show on breasts as a symbol of abundance from the Venus of Willendorf to Cardi B, I ordered ten pounds of bacon. Feels without borders, she said. Right. I dipped my bacon in ice cream and licked the drips off my pajamas as Carnita's side hustle became an empire.

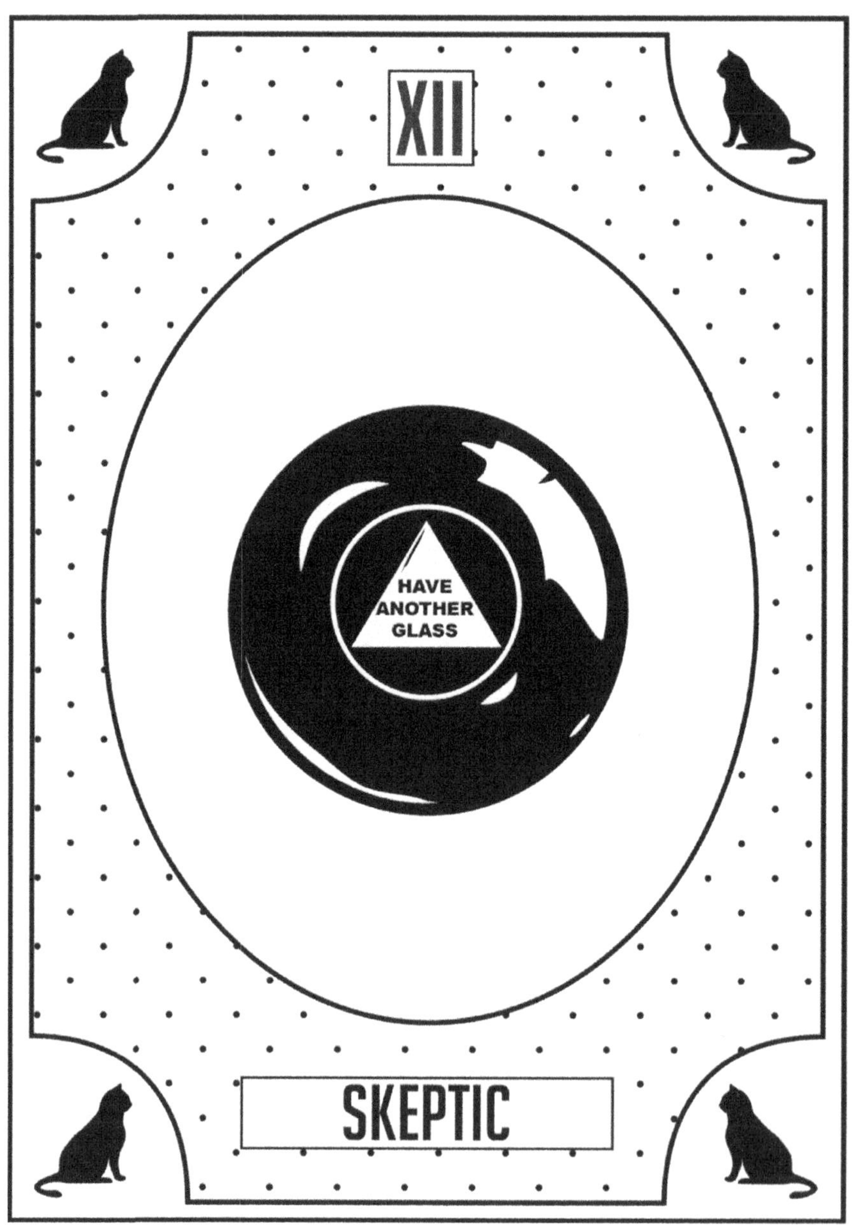
XII
HAVE
ANOTHER
GLASS
SKEPTIC

53. High Risk Behavior

After 32 years of marriage I'm pretty skeptical of monogamy, but maybe that's because I tried it and it didn't work. The thing is, I liked being married the whole time and I really missed being part of a couple when it was suddenly over. For years I searched for the perfect hook-up. Now my lust is contained. I'm in the managed lust program, quite comfortable being single. I have a very nice life with my dog. But as I face the decades ahead and opportunities arise, I have to ask myself if I could be part of a couple again? Is that even a possibility? My inner skeptic slaps her palm on the table and hisses. No, absolutely not. What a ridiculous idea! But my inner romantic has another sip of wine, and half an hour later she's still swirling wine around her glass looking out the window.

I read an article in National Geographic about an isolated tribe of hunter-gatherers who are living today the same way humans lived 10,000 years ago — no government, no religion, no marriage, no monogamy. Women in the tribe are equal to men and couples pair up with no expectation of permanence, and no punishment for infidelity. Men and women have sex based on desire. Children are parented by the whole tribe, and everyone has the same rights. Lifelong commitment to anything but the tribe is unthinkable. Living naked in the bush, chasing down their food with sharp sticks, they can't afford to be idealistic.

But I'm an idealist. That's just who I am. As I consider the possibility of a gender-neutral lifestyle, I'm envious of the egalitarian freedom of those tribe women. I wonder if they ever break into chick fights over a particularly delicious man.

Does sex ever lead them to feel a sense of ownership of their partner? Do they experience love separate from sex? I think about how I was raised, and I wonder how many of my feelings about love and monogamy are cultural conditioning.

Monogamy is not a law of Nature. In Nature diversity rules. The animals who are best at sex dominate the gene pool. Sex is power. We kill for sex. We risk food, shelter, wealth and security for sex. We give up social acceptance, the bonds of family and the stairway to heaven for sex. Sex drives us mad with desire. Sex masquerades as love. Illicit sex cheats us out of a predictable future. Sex is high risk behavior. We endure chaos for sex. We go to jail for sex. Kingdoms are lost and the course of nations diverted because of sex. Sex is basic animal behavior. Even in this modern world, we are still animals.

Why am I even thinking about this? Because I'm reconsidering my opinion on the connection between sex and love, and love and monogamy. What's realistic? Can sex really ever be safe? Is the commitment to love the same as the commitment to monogamy? Or are they two different things? Meanwhile, my inner animal is pacing in her cage and I want out. But it's late in the game for high risk behavior. I need to protect myself. Cynics are warning me that at my age men just want a nurse with a purse. Then I hear poets sing about late life love as polishing the soul. And here I am, still sitting in my chair looking out the window, swirling my wine around my glass, wishing I had a Magic 8-Ball to give me the answers.

I Could Be Wrong

X
MESSENGER

54. Anniversary of Hope

On the longest night I fly among the stars, as far from home as I could be, and I am not afraid up there, gliding through the dark syrup between heaven and Earth. The luscious Solstice lightlessness is music against my skin, a meditation tickling the hair on my arms, passing through me, inside and out of me, spiraling into my ears, sliding against my cheek as I ride the luminescence, witness to mystery. I dream.

Tis the season of angels. They send us messengers. On wings they watch us seek and strive. They announce children to guide us, candles to light our way, remembrance of our history, the battles of our ancestors, a star in the East, shepherds, kings and Little Match Girls, stockings hung with care, the scent of the forest, and choirs billowing bright against the licorice sky.

From the great distance of my dream I see all of it, the realm of my existence. Long nights bathe us in unknowing, washing over us with surrender, respite from the busy light, a retreat from endeavor, a smoothing of the soul into ripples of being, and we are reminded of the roll of time, the ride we are born into, the immutable horizon, the trust we must place in ourselves, the nourishment of sleep. With circadian rhythm the longest nights lift the burden of day. The calendar slows. Our doing dives deep within us.

My strongest recollection of flying is the absence of fear. The weight of gravity lifted from me. I became a constellation of bones. I could see with my heart. Above and below me were one place, and I was without apprehension. There was no falling. My letting go was effortless. I heard no words, no messages, no instructions, no warning, only the shimmer of possibilities, an openness without expectation, the iridescence of promise.

There are many traditions of light in the season of the longest night. Flame holds our gaze with singular focus. We transcend and soften in stories of ancient times, stories of being lost, stories of connecting with our forever selves. These stories give us meaning. The oldest stories told on the longest night guide the flight of our species into the future. Let yourself fly. Explore. Dream. Believe.

I say this with the barest thread of understanding as I mark the place in my mind where neither height, nor weight, nor the clumsiness of my intentions held me back from soaring into the unknown, without fear, unfreckled by doubt, a being with and without form, whole and unto myself, rapt in mystery. On Solstice eve I sail beyond myself into a kingdom of spirits celebrating the sun in repose, freed by the absence of light from the ordinary labors of day to receive the darkness as a gift of rest, the anniversary of hope, and a time to dream of our becoming.

I Could Be Wrong

Billie Best is a Baby Boomer born in 1954 and speaks to her cohort, most particularly women over 50, with her own hard-earned wisdom on life's uncertainty, the renaissance of menopause, fearless aging and coping with ageism. As a professional she has reinvented herself numerous times from the music business to marketing and technology to small scale farming and becoming an author. Her blog "Beyond 60 — Loving Life, Staying Relevant" at billiebest.com has established her as an entertainer, a feminist and a voice for change. Her first book was a memoir titled *How I Made a Huge Mess of My Life (or Couples Therapy with a Dead Man,* from Widowspeak Publishing, March 2020. *I Could Be Wrong* is her second book, an anthology of 54 blog posts released November 2020. Currently she resides in Oregon.

billiebest.com
Facebook.com/billiebest
Instagram.com/billiebestbook
Videos at Vimeo.com/billiebest

Brenda Rose is an artist, designer, and occasional art director living in the Pacific Northwest with her husband and two sons. She loves a good font, vintage ephemera, and has a penchant for clean and simple design with pops of color. Find her work at brendarose.com.

Made in the USA
Coppell, TX
04 December 2020